# THE CONSPIRACY THEORIST'S

## PUZZLE AND ACTIVITY BOOK

### PUZZLING MYSTERIES AND BRAIN-TEASING ACTIVITIES

**JAMIE KING**

summersdale

THE CONSPIRACY THEORIST'S PUZZLE AND ACTIVITY BOOK

Text by Adam Ifans

An Hachette UK Company
www.hachette.co.uk

Summersdale Publishers Ltd
Part of Octopus Publishing Group Limited
Carmelite House
50 Victoria Embankment
LONDON
EC4Y 0DZ
UK

www.summersdale.com

Printed and bound in China

ISBN: 978-1-80007-997-7

Substantial discounts on bulk quantities of Summersdale books are available to corporations, professional associations and other organizations. For details contact general enquiries: telephone: +44 (0) 1243 771107 or email: enquiries@summersdale.com.

# INTRODUCTION

Is the Earth hollow? Does a secret government agency track your every move? Are the British royal family aliens?

If you've picked up this book, it's fair to say you love a good conspiracy theory, as well as a puzzle or ten. That thought may be your own or we may have planted it there using CIA mind control techniques, but either way, *The Conspiracy Theorist's Puzzle and Activity Book* will keep you entertained for hours.

This book features the biggest conspiracy theories from throughout history and an eclectic mix of conundrums, crosswords, wordsearches, sudokus, anagrams and plenty of trivia to test your grasp of what's real and what isn't. So, grab your favourite pen or pencil and settle in somewhere the Men in Black can't find you – there's puzzling to be done!

# DEATH OF A DICTATOR

It's generally accepted that Adolf Hitler killed himself at the end of World War Two. However, a 2009 test on what the Soviet archives claimed to be Hitler's skull showed it actually belonged to a woman. Could that mean he survived after all by secretly escaping before the end of the war?

Solve the clues to find the most popularly theorized escape methods and destinations for the dictator.

**Across**

4. A corpse, twice! (4, 7)

5. The opposite side of the planet to a polar bear (10)

6. Lusitania sinker (5)

**Down**

1. The Police walked on it (3, 4)

2. The second largest country in South America (9)

3. A peppery leaf (6)

# THE OLDEST ARTIFACT IN THE WORLD

In 1991, a prominent geologist and professor at Boston University examined the weathering on the Great Sphinx of Giza in Egypt and concluded that the patterns must have been caused by torrential rain. This would imply that the Sphinx existed before the most ancient of Egyptians, before the very first dynasties — before, in fact, recorded history.

Can you find five differences between the two Sphinxes?

# IMPLANTED MICROCHIPS

Soon, we may no longer have to bother with PINs or passports. Everything about us might be stored in a chip the size of a grain of rice, embedded in our hands, where it can be read or traced through walls and over great distances, tracking our every move.

Match up the microchip symbols. The first one has been done for you.

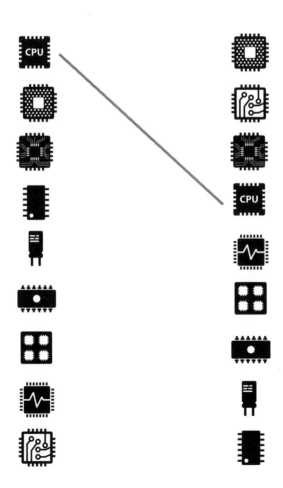

According to some conspiracy theorists, why was Osama bin Laden's assassination a hoax?

## A. He'd been killed several years before

## B. He never existed in the first place

## C. He's still alive and living in Brazil

# WORDSEARCH

# ARE ALIENS SECRETLY IN CHARGE OF THE UK?

The Windsor family were all sheltering from a World War Two Luftwaffe bombing raid when their hideaway was hit. According to one theory, shape-shifting aliens seized this opportunity to assume their identities and infiltrate humankind.

```
J A L I E N H Y B R I D D D O
D I A J A U Z X C V B A N M N
E L A J T I J U I O P V Q Q E
R L Z L A O H H J K K I N C W
H U M A N B L O O D B D O L O
T M G O Q Q B U N H S I D D R
Y I G O W W H J K C V C W N L
U N H P E E Q A S C V K M M D
I A J Q R R Q W E R T E J J S
H T K Q T T L V V X S I I K T
F I L R E P T I L I A N A S A
P R I N C E P H I L I P K K T
X   R S B B S A E E E Q U Y E
T O T A L I T A R I A N L O P
C M O U N T B A T T E N P O N
```

| | | |
|---|---|---|
| ALIEN HYBRID | ILLUMINATI | PRINCE PHILIP |
| DAVID ICKE | MOUNTBATTEN | REPTILIAN |
| HUMAN BLOOD | ONE WORLD STATE | TOTALITARIAN |

$$\text{🐢} \times \text{🐢} = 49$$

$$\text{🐢} + \text{🦅} = 20$$

$$\text{🦅} - \text{🐆} = 10$$

$$\text{🦅} \times \text{🐆} - \text{🐢} = \text{?}$$

# GET THE ALIEN TO ITS SAUCER

Is Area 51 in New Mexico, USA a research centre for investigating UFOs? Some theorize that in the aftermath of the Roswell incident of 1947, when the wreckage of a flying saucer was allegedly recovered from nearby, the ship and its alien crew were taken there for analysis.

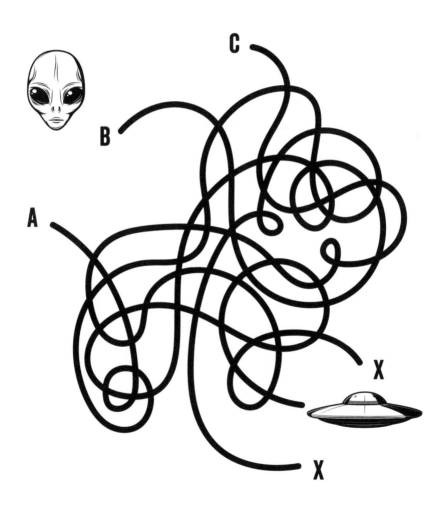

 **BETWEEN THE LINES**

A place that some say doesn't exist can be inserted in the blank line so that, reading downwards, six three-letter words are formed. What is the hidden word between the lines?

| O | D | A | A | B | E | O |
|---|---|---|---|---|---|---|
|   |   |   |   |   |   |   |
| T | G | Y | E | N | D | D |

Who was accused of using subliminal messages during the US presidential election of 2000?

A. Al Gore

B. George W. Bush

C. Bill Clinton

 **HIDDEN WORD**

Can you find the nine-letter word hidden in the grid?

| E | R | A |
|---|---|---|
| M | N | O |
| S | E | F |

Complete the following grid by filling in the empty boxes with the missing numbers.
Each number can only appear once in a row, column or box.

| | 1 | | | | | | 2 | 5 |
|---|---|---|---|---|---|---|---|---|
| | | | | 2 | 6 | | 1 | |
| 2 | | 9 | 1 | | 8 | | | |
| 3 | | 1 | 7 | | 2 | 5 | | 6 |
| | | | 8 | | 3 | 1 | | 2 |
| 8 | | | | 4 | | 7 | | |
| | | 5 | | | 7 | 6 | 3 | |
| 4 | 6 | 2 | 9 | | | | | |
| | 8 | | | 1 | 4 | | 5 | |

 **ACROSTICS**

Solve the clues correctly and the shaded squares will reveal what all conspiracy theorists are seeking.

1. One who attacks civilians
2. Flying machine
3. Disprove
4. Destroyed in 9/11
5. A supernatural presence

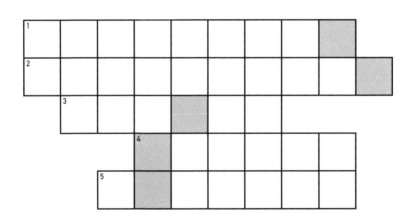

Rearrange these letters to reveal three famous singers whose deaths have triggered conspiracy theories.

# BACK OUR TIN

_ _ _ _ _ _ _ _ _

# LISP SEVERELY

_ _ _ _ _ _ _ _ _ _ _

# JOHN AIMS CACKLE

_ _ _ _ _ _ _ _ _ _ _ _

 **WORDSEARCH**

# DOES JESUS' BLOODLINE SURVIVE TO THIS DAY?

According to the Jesus bloodline conspiracy, Jesus was human, not an otherworldly figure who was resurrected post-crucifixion. It is claimed that he was married with children and that his descendants have walked the Earth ever since.

```
C  A  R  P  E  N  T  E  R  E  E  R  T  Y  B
A  A  S  V  C  H  R  I  S  T  I  A  N  M  L
M  P  Q  E  R  T  U  G  D  F  C  A  A  C  O
M  I  O  A  A  M  S  D  F  I  R  A  R  R  O
A  H  H  S  D  F  L  I  E  R  U  V  B  J  D
G  A  S  D  T  W  D  B  N  N  C  A  S  D  L
D  J  H  G  F  L  E  E  O  I  I  D  D  K  I
A  Q  W  E  R  E  E  T  Y  U  F  I  O  K  N
L  A  S  D  F  O  H  J  K  L  I  B  B  C  E
E  S  S  U  I  N  S  S  D  L  X  K  K  K  O
N  Y  T  R  W  A  Q  Q  Q  S  I  X  X  U  Y
E  A  S  P  R  I  O  R  Y  O  F  S  I  O  N
H  J  K  O  U  D  Q  Q  B  B  N  J  K  L  M
J  J  I  O  H  O  L  Y  G  R  A  I  L  W  E
T  Y  U  I  G  F  D  S  A  K  L  E  E  R  S
```

| APOSTLE | CHRISTIAN | LEONARDO |
|---------|-----------|----------|
| BLOODLINE | CRUCIFIXION | MAGDALENE |
| CARPENTER | HOLY GRAIL | PRIORY OF SION |

See how many words of four or more letters you can make, using each letter only once. Each word must use the central letter. Can you find the word that uses all of the letters?

# TRUMP'S WINDMILLS

Wind turbines are widely regarded as a safe and sustainable way to generate electricity, but it seems that former president Donald Trump does not agree. At the National Republican Congressional Committee's annual spring dinner in Washington in 2019, conspiracy theories started to fly when he quipped, "They say the noise [of the wind turbines] causes cancer."

Match up the energy symbols. The first one has been done for you.

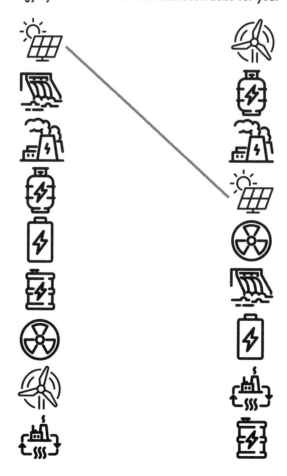

Some say the Shroud of Turin bears the imprint of Jesus after his crucifixion. The cloth shows the image of a bearded man with injuries similar to those associated with being crucified. The position of the nail wounds, however, raise suspicions about the authenticity of the shroud. Where are they?

A. In his palms

B. In his wrists

C. In his feet

 **CROSSWORD**

# A DEADLY VIRUS

The Severe Acute Respiratory Syndrome (SARS) virus appeared in 2002, quickly spreading panic across the world. Over 8,000 cases and almost 800 deaths were reported within a year. But was SARS a naturally occurring pandemic or something more sinister? Theorists have pointed the finger at the US and Chinese governments, as well as a shady cabal called the New World Order.

Solve the clues to find the theories about how and why this terrible virus was allegedly created.

## Across

2. Experimental facility (10)

4. Fluke (8)

5. Not of natural origin (7)

6. Organic instrument of death (9)

## Down

1. Too many people (14)

3. In the crosshairs (8)

# WORD WHEEL

See how many words of four or more letters you can make, using each letter only once. Each word must use the central letter. Can you find the word that uses all of the letters?

# BLACK HELICOPTERS

Some believe that mysterious black helicopters are pursuing and terrifying completely innocent victims across the USA. The helicopters have also been linked with a number of cases of cattle mutilation over the years, as these mysterious aircraft have been seen in immediate proximity before, during or after this bizarre crime has taken place.

Can you spot the five differences between the two black helicopter images below?

# GET THE DEMON TO THE PORTAL

Could the Large Hadron Collider at the France–Switzerland border open a gateway between Hell and Earth? Fears about this peaked in June 2016 when photos emerged of an alarming lightning storm located directly above the LHC — was this just the start?

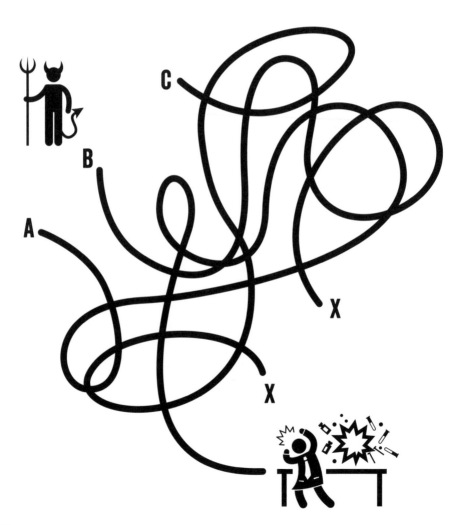

Alleged evidence of chemical poisoning can be inserted in the blank line so that, reading downwards, ten three-letter words are formed. What is the hidden word between the lines?

| A | T | P | A | S | T | L | P | A | U |
|---|---|---|---|---|---|---|---|---|---|
|   |   |   |   |   |   |   |   |   |   |
| E | E | N | P | Y | Y | B | N | E | E |

Can you find the nine-letter word hidden in the grid?

| E | T | U |
|---|---|---|
| B | S | C |
| E | A | D |

 **ANAGRAMS**

Rearrange these letters to reveal three clandestine organizations.

# SAFER OMENS

_ _ _ _ _ _ _ _ _ _

# AIM TILL UNI

_ _ _ _ _ _ _ _ _ _

# DROWN ELDER ROW

_ _ _ _ _ _ _ _ _ _ _ _

$$\text{🛰️} - \text{👨‍🚀} = 4$$

$$\text{🪐} + \text{🪐} = 20$$

$$\text{🪐} + \text{👨‍🚀} = 13$$

$$\text{👨‍🚀} \times \text{🛰️} - \text{🪐} = \text{?}$$

 **CROSSWORD**

# AUTOMATED ASSASSINS

MK-Ultra is believed to have been a clandestine mind control programme ran by the US Central Intelligence Agency (CIA). It was supposedly launched in the early 1950s and was based on the work of Nazi scientists. It is speculated that the CIA trained assassins to be totally subservient to their masters' wishes and incapable of recalling any act they had committed.

Solve the clues to find the methods the CIA allegedly used to control their subjects' minds.

Across

2. Lightning surprise (12)
4. Mesmerism (8)
5. Acid (3)
6. Mary Jane (9)

Down

1. Cleaning your mind (12)
3. Waterfowl with an extra eye (6)

**Solve the clues correctly and the shaded squares will reveal a famous submarine.**

1. It will always float

2. The cause of a cold

3. Speculate about something

4. Where Mars is

5. Sir

— — — — —

# GET THE SPY TO THE PHONE

On a typical day, thousands of telephone calls are legally recorded by authorities. But how many calls are being eavesdropped on illegally? In some countries, every international phone call may be recorded and monitored.

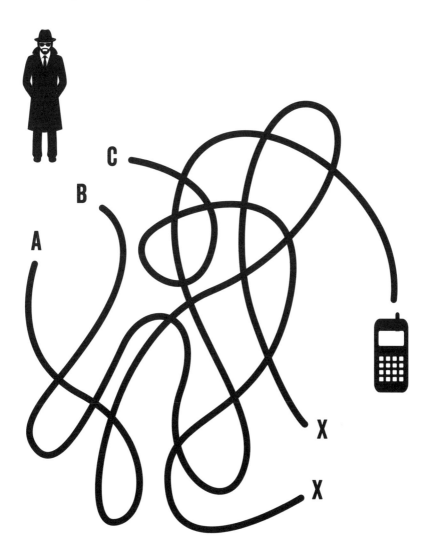

# SPOT THE DIFFERENCE

# A ROBOTIC PRESIDENT

Many people have theorized that former US president Bill Clinton is not what he appears to be. Some have gone so far as to suggest that he is neither a human nor a reptilian alien, but is actually a robot jointly operated by the FBI and a certain famous cartoon company.

Can you spot the five differences between the two robot images below?

 # WORD WHEEL

See how many words of four or more letters you can make, using each letter only once. Each word must use the central letter. Can you find the word that uses all of the letters?

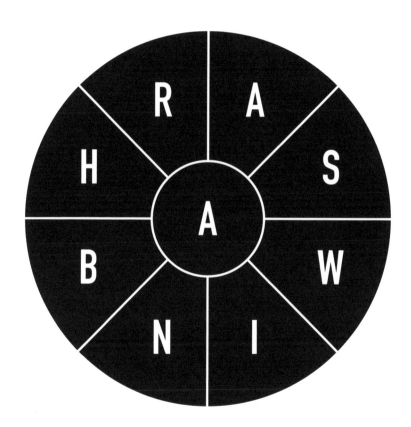

# BETWEEN THE LINES

A global intelligence network which became public knowledge in the 1980s can be inserted in the blank line so that, reading downwards, seven three-letter words are formed. What is the hidden word between the lines?

| B | A | S | L | A | B | I |
|---|---|---|---|---|---|---|
|   |   |   |   |   |   |   |
| G | T | Y | G | L | O | K |

 **WORDSEARCH**

# WHAT REALLY HAPPENED AT CHERNOBYL?

Did the huge explosion at the Chernobyl nuclear power plant in 1986 happen because the reactor had purposefully been pushed into an extremely dangerous situation? Some theorize that the disaster was an experiment in preparation for fighting a nuclear war.

```
A C C R T Y U I O P G V B N M
S H O O O E X P L O S I O N E
D A N L A A A L L I I G F U L
F I T F D Q A S D F G H J C T
G N R B B W Q Q G H J K L L D
H R O A S D A H G F D S K E O
J E L M K L G R D E R T Y A W
K A R E A C T O R D T T Y R N
L C O A O O I M J U I M H H
Q T D Q A W E U R T Y U I O J
W I S S D F I I O U Q A E D F
E O Q W E N G B N M K J H G F
R N A S A W Q S S S Y U I O P
T E I R A Q W S G J K L I O P
Y I U K R A I N E E K U R I E
```

CHAIN REACTION       EXPLOSION       REACTOR
COLD WAR             MELTDOWN        UKRAINE
CONTROL RODS         NUCLEAR         URANIUM

Can you find the nine-letter word hidden in the grid?

| | | |
|---|---|---|
| B | L | V |
| I | S | E |
| E | R | E |

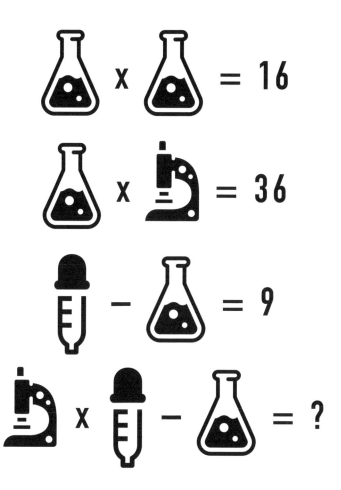

# ACROSTICS

Solve the clues correctly and the shaded squares will reveal the uniform choice of some mysterious agents.

1. A secret faction

2. Between the UK and the USA

3. A vicious whirlwind

4. A computer brain

5. Stole a person

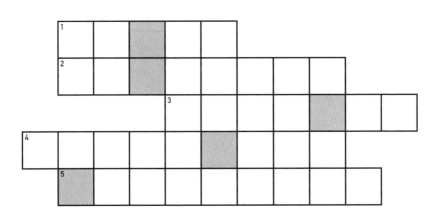

On 9/11, geological readings led many people to the conclusion that the towers were blown up with explosives planted directly underneath the buildings and not by the enormous volume of fuel that ignited after the two airliners exploded. When did the geological surveys in New York record the greatest amount of seismic activity?

## A. Immediately before the Twin Towers collapsed

## B. As the Twin Towers were collapsing

## C. Three and a half minutes after the final collapse

Complete the following grid by filling in the empty boxes with the missing numbers. Each number can only appear once in a row, column or box.

| 1 |   | 7 |   |   | 6 | 4 |   |   |
|---|---|---|---|---|---|---|---|---|
| 5 | 6 |   |   |   |   | 9 | 7 | 3 |
| 4 | 9 |   |   | 8 | 7 |   | 1 |   |
| 9 |   | 6 |   | 3 | 8 | 1 |   |   |
| 7 | 8 |   |   | 1 | 4 |   | 5 |   |
|   | 1 | 4 | 9 |   | 5 | 6 | 2 | 8 |
| 6 | 7 |   |   | 5 |   |   |   |   |
|   | 3 |   | 7 |   |   | 5 |   |   |
| 2 | 4 |   |   | 6 |   | 7 |   | 1 |

 # ANAGRAMS

Rearrange these letters to reveal three names for visitors from elsewhere.

## RATTER RELATRIXES

_ _ _ _ _ _ _ _ _ _ _ _ _ _ _ _ _

## ARMAN IT

_ _ _ _ _ _ _

## AVIE NUNS

_ _ _ _ _ _ _ _

# FLYING SAUCERS

Witnesses testify that particularly high numbers of UFOs are spotted around military bases worldwide. In the USA, there is a theory that aliens either visit, or are kept in, Area 51 — a rumour that has been in circulation since the infamous Roswell incident of 1947.

Match up the UFO symbols. The first one has been done for you.

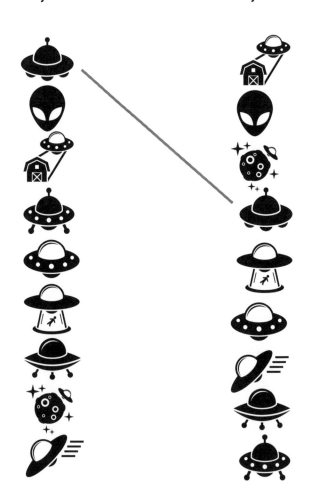

Can you find the nine-letter word hidden in the grid?

| | | |
|:---:|:---:|:---:|
| I | M | C |
| T | A | R |
| U | B | E |

# GET THE PRESIDENT TO THE WMDS

Many believe that George W. Bush lied about the weapons of mass destruction (WMDs) that were the official reason for the American invasion of Iraq. The theory is this: he wanted revenge because, after the Gulf War, Saddam Hussein was reportedly sending death threats to Bush's father, George H.W. Bush Sr.

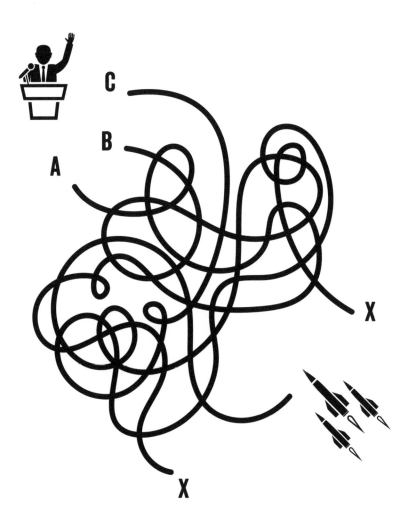

$$\text{〰} + \text{🦆} = 9$$

$$\triangle - \text{〰} = 18$$

$$\text{🦆} \times \text{🦆} = 49$$

$$\triangle \div \text{〰} - \text{🦆} = \,?$$

# BETWEEN THE LINES

A controversial chemical can be inserted in the blank line so that, reading downwards, eight three-letter words are formed. What is the hidden word between the lines?

| A | O | H | P | O | D | A | M |
|---|---|---|---|---|---|---|---|
|   |   |   |   |   |   |   |   |
| T | D | T | D | B | D | D | N |

# THE EVERLASTING LIGHT BULB

Theorists speculate that an everlasting light bulb was invented many years ago but was suppressed in order to make the public continue buying disposable products.

Match up the light bulb symbols. The first one has been done for you.

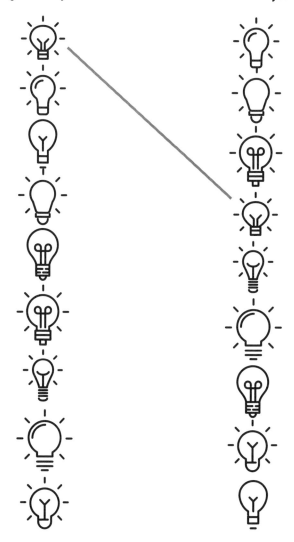

# IS GLOBAL WARMING ONE OF HISTORY'S GREATEST EVER HOAXES?

According to one theory, the "global warming" agenda is all part of a plan sponsored by the United Nations to redistribute wealth by stunting industrial development in the West, in favour of the expansion of major emerging world markets, such as China, Brazil and India.

```
C  L  I  M  A  T  E  A  S  Q  V  B  W  J  J
A  D  A  Q  A  Q  N  S  A  A  O  Q  I  Q  G
D  S  S  A  S  A  V  T  P  Q  Z  A  N  W  R
F  A  H  Z  D  S  I  Y  A  F  O  S  D  E  E
G  S  J  Z  F  D  R  U  R  G  N  D  P  R  E
H  D  K  F  G  F  O  I  I  H  E  F  O  T  N
J  F  L  E  H  G  N  O  S  J  Q  G  W  Y  H
K  G  V  D  J  H  M  P  A  K  A  H  E  U  O
K  K  B  T  K  J  E  P  S  L  S  J  R  I  U
L  I  N  H  L  K  N  X  H  P  X  K  S  O  S
I  O  M  J  I  L  T  F  T  O  F  O  V  A  E
O  P  L  I  I  O  D  G  I  R  G  I  H  S  A
P  K  Y  O  T  O  S  H  O  E  E  U  I  D  A
R  R  R  K  O  O  I  J  P  R  J  M  O  F  A
S  R  U  L  F  O  S  S  I  L  F  U  E  L  A
```

| CLIMATE | FOSSIL FUEL | OZONE |
|---|---|---|
| ENVIRONMENT | GREENHOUSE | PARIS |
| EXTREME | KYOTO | WIND POWER |

Some theorists suggest that the US government was responsible for the devastating tsunami that struck Southeast Asia on 26 December 2004. What do they believe triggered the tsunami?

A. Directed-energy weapon

B. Nuclear bomb

C. Cloud seeding

# ACROSTICS

Solve the clues correctly and the shaded squares will reveal something not of this Earth.

1. A secret plot
2. Aluminium, for example
3. Planet with a red spot
4. Town in New Mexico
5. Otherworldly

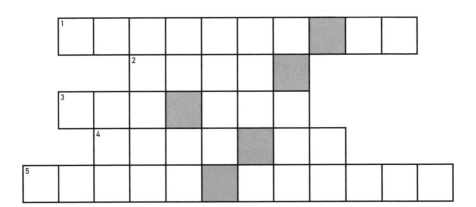

— — — — —

 # WORD WHEEL

See how many words of four or more letters you can make, using each letter only once. Each word must use the central letter. Can you find the word that uses all of the letters?

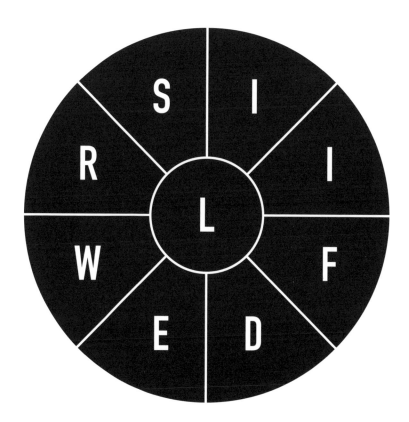

Can you find the nine-letter word hidden in the grid?

| | | |
|---|---|---|
| I | P | D |
| N | A | P |
| D | K | E |

 **CROSSWORD**

# FLAT AS A PANCAKE

Some flat-earthers believe that the truth about our planet's shape is being covered up in a "round Earth conspiracy" coordinated by NASA and government agencies. According to them, the Earth is in fact a disc with the Arctic Circle in its centre, while Antarctica, a 150 ft tall wall of ice, sits around the rim.

Solve the clues to find the numerous alleged fakes created by the so-called "round Earth conspiracy".

### Across

4. One small step for Neil (4, 7)

5. The Milky Way and friends (8)

6. They circle the sun (7)

### Down

1. High-flying pilot (9)

2. This keeps you grounded (7)

3. Something in orbit (9)

# SUDOKU

Complete the following grid by filling in the empty boxes with the missing numbers. Each number can only appear once in a row, column or box.

| | | 2 | | | 8 | | 3 | 9 |
|---|---|---|---|---|---|---|---|---|
| | | 9 | | | 5 | | | 1 |
| | 8 | 5 | | | 3 | | 6 | 7 |
| 2 | 5 | | 9 | | | 6 | 7 | 3 |
| 4 | 3 | 7 | 5 | 8 | 6 | | | 2 |
| | | 1 | | 2 | 7 | 8 | | 4 |
| 5 | 9 | 3 | 4 | | | | 1 | |
| | | | | | 9 | | | |
| | | | | | 1 | | | 5 |

 **ANAGRAMS**

Rearrange these letters to reveal three assassination weapons.

# CRAB MOB

_ _ _ _ _ _ _

# REFLECT POLICIES

_ _ _ _ _ _ _ _ _ _ _ _ _ _ _

# ANTHILL EJECTION

_ _ _ _ _ _ _ _ _ _ _ _ _ _ _

# BETWEEN THE LINES

A powerful cabal can be inserted in the blank line so that, reading downwards, ten three-letter words are formed. What is the hidden word between the lines?

| A | A | A | G | E | G | A | G | A | G |
|---|---|---|---|---|---|---|---|---|---|
|   |   |   |   |   |   |   |   |   |   |
| L | E | P | T | U | N | Y | S | E | G |

See how many words of four or more letters you can make, using each letter only once. Each word must use the central letter. Can you find the word that uses all of the letters?

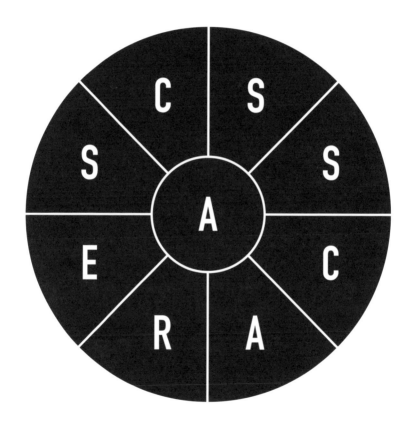

# GET THE MARTIANS TO THE PYRAMID

Startling evidence has shown that intelligent life may have set foot on Mars at some stage in the past. Photographs of remarkable pyramid-like structures have come back from the planet, structures that seem not only to be artificially constructed but bear a similar "face" to that of the Great Sphinx of Giza.

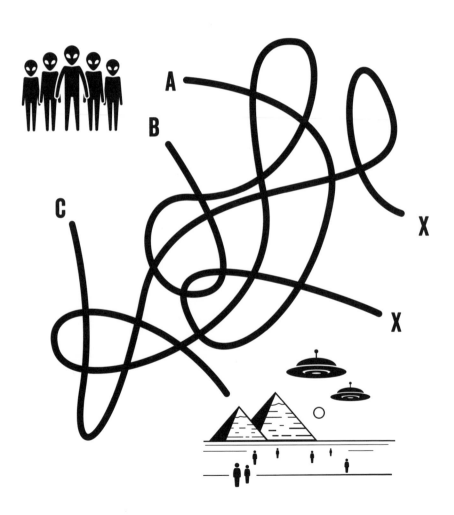

 **ACROSTICS**

Solve the clues correctly and the shaded squares will reveal a fatal disease.

1. Inoculate a population
2. Rocket launch
3. At the centre of Pizzagate
4. Pretence
5. Vanish without trace

— — — — —

In 2013, a huge meteor was spotted descending toward Russia and exploding in a massive ball of flame over the Chelyabinsk region. What do some theorists believe caused the meteor?

A. Radioactive satellite falling from orbit

B. A computer game manifesting in real life

C. Part of the moon detaching

 **CROSSWORD**

# DISASTER AT SEA

In 1912, RMS *Titanic* sank to the bottom of the North Atlantic, taking two-thirds of its passengers to their icy deaths. The disaster has long been attributed to a collision with an iceberg, but recent examination of the hull gave rise to a different theory: was the *Titanic* sunk by a torpedo from a German U-boat?

Solve the clues to find the key facts about this most famous of ships.

### Across

2. Kirk, Hook and Marvel (7)

4. All aboard! (10)

5. A girl's journey (6, 6)

### Down

1. Rescue crafts (9)

3. Always buoyant (10)

6. The pond (8)

# WAS "NEW COKE" DESIGNED TO FAIL?

In 1985, the Coca-Cola Company introduced a new version of their drink, dubbed "New Coke". It did not do well, and the company quickly backtracked. One theory is that the switch was designed to hide the change from using cane sugar in classic Coke to using the far cheaper high-fructose corn syrup, which would alter the taste, if only slightly.

```
O  T  H  E  R  E  A  L  T  H  I  N  G  O  C
T  F  O  R  M  U  L  A  O  P  N  E  F  O  L
A  C  K  O  E  V  U  M  L  A  S  D  F  G  A
S  Q  W  E  R  T  Y  U  N  F  G  G  J  K  S
T  B  F  T  O  O  K  E  E  C  I  K  E  S  S
E  V  F  R  T  Y  U  S  W  E  E  T  E  R  I
T  S  W  E  E  F  E  Z  C  K  C  G  E  R  C
E  K  E  O  C  D  F  G  O  Q  W  E  T  Y  C
S  C  O  C  A  I  M  C  K  G  H  J  K  L  O
T  Q  W  E  R  T  Y  H  E  J  K  I  O  P  K
Q  W  E  R  T  R  V  B  N  M  S  S  K  K  E
I  I  R  R  R  C  V  B  N  M  F  G  H  Y  U
Q  W  E  E  R  T  Y  U  I  J  K  L  L  C  C
C  O  H  E  C  O  R  N  S  Y  R  U  P  K  E
I  C  A  N  E  S  U  G  A  R  S  U  G  R  E
```

| | | |
|---|---|---|
| CANE SUGAR | CORN SYRUP | SWEETER |
| CHERRY COKE | FORMULA | TASTE TEST |
| CLASSIC COKE | NEW COKE | THE REAL THING |

# SECRET LABORATORIES

As the COVID-19 outbreak turned into a global pandemic, a sinister theory began to circulate that a laboratory in Wuhan had invented the virus as a bioweapon. Many pointed to the fact that the Institute of Virology, which houses China's first level-4 biosafety laboratory (the highest classification of labs that study deadly viruses), is situated in Wuhan.

Match up the laboratory symbols. The first one has been done for you.

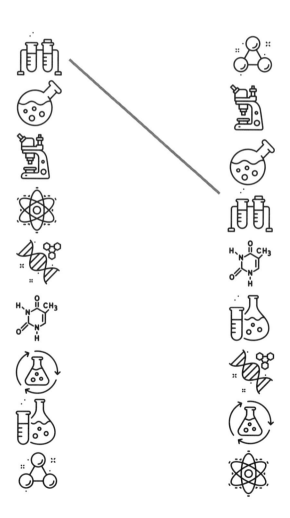

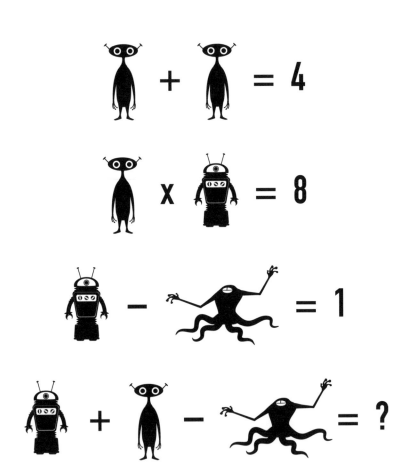

 **ANAGRAMS**

Rearrange these letters to reveal powers of the mind.

# HYPE LATTE

_ _ _ _ _ _ _ _ _

# SLEEK IN SITE

_ _ _ _ _ _ _ _ _ _

# INCEPTION ORG

_ _ _ _ _ _ _ _ _ _ _

# A SOCIETY WITH A SECRET

Freemasonry is a well-known, worldwide fraternity that is dedicated to charitable work and the promotion of moral correctness. Some speculate that this secret society is a cover for the Illuminati, a powerful group of prominent figures believed to exert covert control over many important aspects of government and society.

Can you spot the five differences between the two masonic images below?

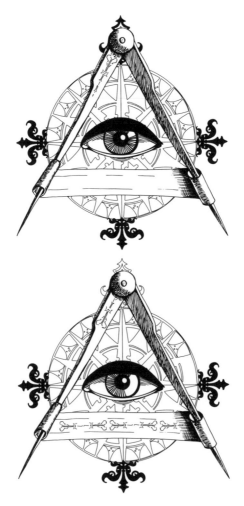

Barack Obama, the USA's first Black president, has attracted more than his fair share of conspiracy theories. According to some theorists, what explains his secret hatred of the country he led?

A. He is a devout Buddhist

B. He was born in Canada

C. He is secretly an Islamic extremist

# GET THE GHOST TO THE COMPUTER

According to simulation theories, all of reality, including the Earth and universe, is a computer-generated simulation that is realistic enough to convince its inhabitants it is real. It is believed that ghost hauntings and alien sightings are simply glitches in this simulation.

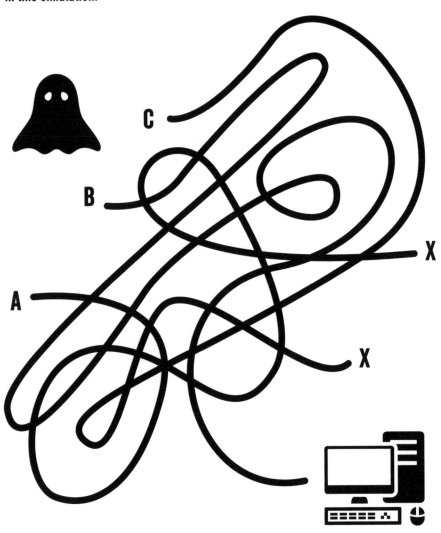

This controversial treatment can be inserted in the blank line so that, reading downwards, seven three-letter words are formed. What is the hidden word between the lines?

| O | B | A | I | L | E | S |
|---|---|---|---|---|---|---|
|   |   |   |   |   |   |   |
| A | D | T | E | D | D | T |

# THE PIZZAGATE CONSPIRACY

In 2016, theorists began to speculate about the link between the Comet Ping Pong pizzeria in Washington, D.C. and the Democratic Party, culminating in the (now widely debunked) conclusion that Comet Ping Pong was the base for a child abuse ring.

Match up the pizza symbols. The first one has been done for you.

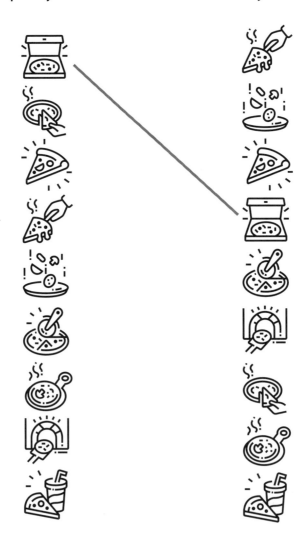

According to some, for what reason did corporate executives devise the hip-hop music genre?

A. To increase sales of tasers

B. To boost profit margins of drug cartels

C. To keep private prisons full

$$\heartsuit + \text{pill} = 24$$

$$\text{pill} - \text{syringe} = 18$$

$$\heartsuit \times \heartsuit = 25$$

$$\text{pill} + \text{syringe} - \heartsuit = ?$$

 **HIDDEN WORD**

Can you find the nine-letter word hidden in the grid?

| | | |
|---|---|---|
| P | I | I |
| H | C | O |
| M | R | C |

Rearrange these letters to reveal how Big Brother is tracking you.

## ARTICLES ON WOKS

_ _ _ _ _ _ _ _ _ _ _ _ _ _ _

## SHARPEN TOMS

_ _ _ _ _ _ _ _ _ _ _

## DART DISC REC

_ _ _ _ _ _ _ _ _ _ _

# A SECRET DESERT AIRBASE

Area 51 in the Nevada desert has become infamous for its secrecy and strange goings-on. The official line is that the area is a military testing facility, but some theorize that it is a research centre for investigating UFOs, such as the one that allegedly crashed near Roswell in 1947.

Can you spot the five differences between the two UFO images below?

Complete the following grid by filling in the empty boxes with the missing numbers. Each number can only appear once in a row, column or box.

| 8 |   |   |   | 9 | 4 | 3 | 5 | 1 |
|---|---|---|---|---|---|---|---|---|
| 9 |   |   | 6 |   |   | 8 |   |   |
|   |   |   | 3 |   | 2 | 9 | 7 | 6 |
| 4 |   |   | 9 | 3 | 6 | 1 |   |   |
| 7 |   | 3 | 5 | 4 |   |   |   | 9 |
| 6 | 9 |   |   | 7 |   |   |   | 5 |
|   |   | 5 |   |   | 7 |   | 9 | 8 |
| 1 |   |   |   |   | 3 |   | 2 |   |
| 2 | 6 |   | 4 | 5 |   |   |   | 3 |

 **ACROSTICS**

Solve the clues correctly and the shaded squares will reveal an ex-KGB agent.

1. Authorized to perform rites
2. Airless
3. Violent act
4. Look into
5. Proverbially hard to find

— — — — —

# WAS BRUCE LEE ASSASSINATED?

Bruce Lee was laid to rest in Lake View Cemetery in Seattle, USA on 31 July 1973. But long before his sudden and tragic death at the age of 32, rumours were rife that he had been dead for months, with his demise blamed on Hong Kong triads, the Mafia, drug abuse and a former martial arts teacher.

```
S Q W E R T Y U O H P P T G G
E C S G Y H U J I O W S D E R
N O I U S D F G H N Z X C V E
S A S D F G T H N G Z X F T E
E G H J K L U Y I K A Q W E N
I A G H J K L W O O Q A S D H
J K U N G F U O O N A G H H O
R T Y U I V B F G G A K L L R
T P R E S S U R E P O I N T N
B R U C E L E E X C C J I K E
A S D N J I O P E D F G R E T
M A R T I A L A R T S A Z C F
A S D F D M O V I E S T A R Q
Q A S D F G H H Y U I O T N H
W A C T I O N H E R O W W W W
```

ACTION HERO
BRUCE LEE
GREEN HORNET

HONG KONG
KUNG FU
MARTIAL ARTS

MOVIE STAR
PRESSURE POINT
SENSEI

 # WORD WHEEL

See how many words of four or more letters you can make, using each letter only once. Each word must use the central letter. Can you find the word that uses all of the letters?

# BETWEEN THE LINES

The victim of a suspicious shooting can be inserted in the blank line so that, reading downwards, six three-letter words are formed. What is the hidden word between the lines?

| O | D | E | A | S | O |
|---|---|---|---|---|---|
|   |   |   |   |   |   |
| D | N | D | Y | B | E |

 **ANAGRAMS**

Rearrange these letters to reveal three famous targets of assassination.

# ABANDONS EMAIL

— — — — — — — — — — — — —

# MURK TIN EARTHLING

— — — — — — — — — — — — — — —

# JENNY FED HONK

— — — — — — — — — — —

# GUY FAWKES AND OTHER PLOTTERS

On 5 November 1605, 36 barrels of gunpowder were found beneath the Houses of Parliament in London, UK. While Guy Fawkes has been popularized as the culprit, one alternative theory is that Robert Cecil, the Earl of Salisbury, was the real mastermind, planning it so that he could paint the Catholics in a bad light.

Can you spot the five differences between the two Big Ben images below?

# PUT THE MICROCHIP IN THE VACCINE

In 2020, a conspiracy theory about vaccines spread almost as quickly as the COVID-19 virus itself. The unlikely claim is that the coronavirus epidemic is a cover for a secret organization, masterminded by Microsoft owner Bill Gates, to implant trackable microchips in the world's population through vaccination.

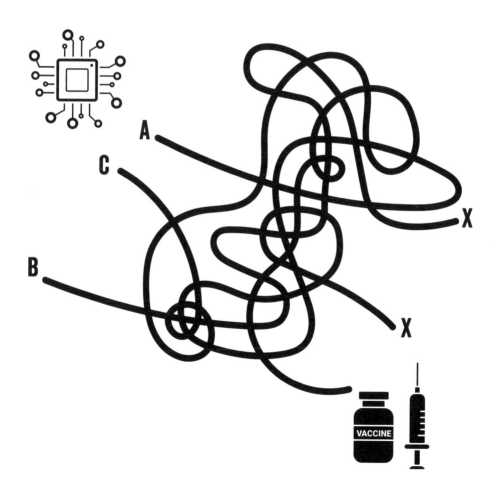

Between 4–16 September 1999, five bombs exploded in four apartment buildings in Moscow, Buynaksk and Volgodonsk, claiming nearly 300 lives and injuring hundreds more. Many believe that the bombings were orchestrated by the Russian Federal Security Service, but for what reason?

A. To help Vladimir Putin become president

B. To help Boris Yeltsin become president

C. To divert attention from a government scandal

🏦 + 🏦 = 18

🏦 × 💰 = 9

💰 ÷ 🪙 = 1

💰 × 🪙 × 🏦 = ?

# AN INJECTION OF CONTROVERSY

There are those who believe that the MMR vaccine, given to every child in the UK, causes autism. In 1998, this theory seemed to be backed up by a scientific paper in *The Lancet* by Andrew Wakefield, but he has since admitted that it was not based on any solid evidence.

Match up the vaccination symbols. The first one has been done for you.

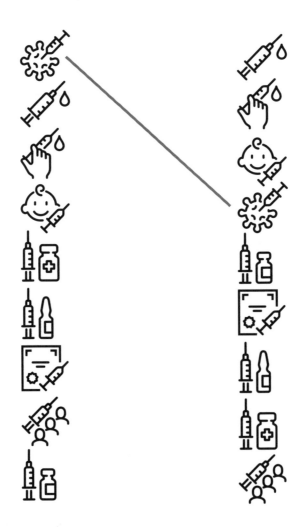

 # WORD WHEEL

See how many words of four or more letters you can make, using each letter only once. Each word must use the central letter. Can you find the word that uses all of the letters?

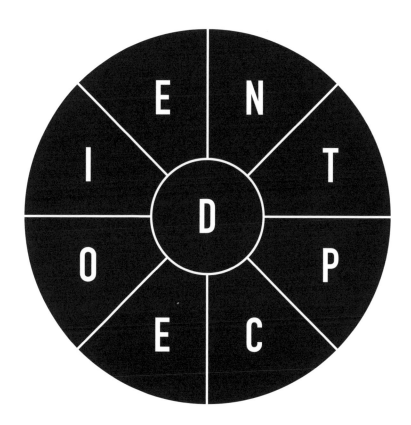

# ACROSTICS

**Solve the clues correctly and the shaded squares will reveal a secretive organization.**

1. Stalin, for example
2. She flooded New Orleans in 2005
3. Armed conflict
4. Large ape-like creature
5. First to the moon

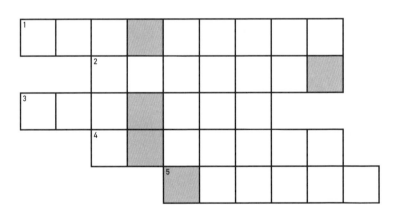

— — — — —

$$\text{target} - \text{grenade} = 5$$

$$\text{pistol} \times \text{target} = 14$$

$$\text{pistol} \times \text{pistol} = 1$$

$$\text{target} + \text{grenade} - \text{pistol} = \ ?$$

Can you find the nine-letter word hidden in the grid?

| | | |
|:---:|:---:|:---:|
| D | U | K |
| E | N | I |
| G | N | B |

Insert an incredible event that many believed never happened in the blank line so that, reading downwards, eleven three-letter words are formed. What is the hidden phrase between the lines?

| A | L | H | A | F | M | G | A | P | I | A |
|---|---|---|---|---|---|---|---|---|---|---|
|   |   |   |   |   |   |   |   |   |   |   |
| P | G | T | D | Y | T | U | D | N | N | E |

# DID THE BRITISH GOVERNMENT WEAPONIZE CLOUD SEEDING?

In 1952, 90 million tons of water flooded the village of Lynmouth in Devon, UK, claiming 34 lives. Theorists believe that the rain-making experiments of the government initiative Project Cumulus may have caused the flooding.

```
W  C  L  O  U  D  S  E  E  D  I  N  G  W  P
E  O  U  Q  W  E  R  T  E  D  F  G  H  L  R
A  P  N  M  T  E  Q  I  X  Q  Q  Y  J  Y  O
T  R  N  E  L  I  A  O  P  W  A  Y  H  N  J
H  E  N  T  F  O  E  I  E  E  Z  U  G  M  E
E  C  N  E  G  S  N  I  R  R  X  I  F  O  C
R  I  N  O  H  T  F  I  I  T  D  O  D  U  T
C  P  N  R  J  H  G  E  M  Y  V  P  S  T  C
O  I  Y  O  K  J  H  R  E  B  G  Q  A  H  U
N  T  T  L  O  K  J  T  N  U  U  W  L  U  M
T  A  R  O  O  L  K  Y  T  N  H  S  O  R  U
R  T  E  G  P  M  L  U  L  N  J  E  P  T  L
O  I  O  Y  Q  A  L  U  I  I  K  B  U  I  U
L  O  S  I  L  V  E  R  I  O  D  I  D  E  S
O  N  C  U  M  U  L  O  N  I  M  B  U  S  N
```

| CLOUD SEEDING | LYNMOUTH | PROJECT CUMULUS |
| CUMULONIMBUS | METEOROLOGY | SILVER IODIDE |
| EXPERIMENT | PRECIPITATION | WEATHER CONTROL |

# PYRAMIDS FROM THE STARS

Were the ancient Egyptians aided in the creation of the pyramids and the Sphinx by superior technology from outer space? Or is this theory itself part of a greater conspiracy intended to make humanity feel subordinate to a superior extraterrestrial race with plans to rule the Earth?

Match up the Egyptian symbols. The first one has been done for you.

# DEATH OF A BOMBSHELL

Marilyn Monroe died in 1962 at the age of 36. The official ruling was that the Hollywood star committed suicide by a drug overdose, however, many believe her death was anything but straightforward. It is suspected that there were a large number of people who wanted to be rid of her for one reason or another.

Solve the clues to find the alleged suspects in Monroe's untimely death.

**Across**

5. Set loose bricklayers (10)

6. They recite the Hippocratic Oath (6)

**Down**

1. Domestic manager (11)

2. Saline (anag.) (6)

3. Youngest elected US president (7)

4. *The Sopranos* (5)

# GET THE PIG DNA INTO THE VIRUS

Swine flu was first reported in Mexico in April 2009 before spreading across the world and claiming thousands of lives. But did this pandemic occur naturally? One theory is that the virus was created by a research-based pharmaceutical industry cartel in order to generate much-needed revenue.

# WORDSEARCH

# ARE TRAILER PARKS DESIGNED TO CULL THE POPULATION?

After the Great Depression, US president Franklin D. Roosevelt embarked on a huge social reform project intended to rehabilitate the country's economy. Theorists suggest that Roosevelt secretly created the trailer parks in areas with abnormally high incidences of tornadoes to help keep population numbers under control.

```
O  I  D  A  S  D  F  Y  U  O  S  X  X  I  T
O  V  E  R  P  O  P  U  L  A  T  I  O  N  O
A  S  P  C  T  Y  U  I  O  O  P  T  R  E  R
P  N  R  W  O  I  O  P  I  O  O  W  E  C  N
R  J  E  E  S  N  Q  W  D  F  G  E  J  K  A
E  I  S  R  E  N  O  Y  O  R  O  L  Q  Q  D
S  B  S  F  D  N  Q  M  P  D  O  F  Z  X  O
I  G  I  G  F  I  W  W  Y  F  S  A  A  Y  E
D  D  O  H  G  U  E  E  Q  T  T  R  W  H  S
E  E  N  J  H  P  R  R  W  G  H  E  S  J  Q
N  Y  D  K  J  O  T  T  E  Y  I  I  E  U  S
T  U  R  O  O  S  E  V  E  L  T  I  D  U  W
E  I  O  D  K  Y  Y  U  I  I  L  U  R  U  D
D  O  T  R  A  I  L  E  R  P  A  R  K  U  F
S  T  O  C  K  M  A  R  K  E  T  R  Y  P  I
```

| DEPRESSION | PRESIDENT | TORNADOES |
| --- | --- | --- |
| ECONOMY | ROOSEVELT | TRAILER PARK |
| OVERPOPULATION | STOCK MARKET | WELFARE |

Why do some theorists believe that Elizabeth I never married?

A. She was a robot pretending to be Elizabeth

B. She was a man pretending to be Elizabeth

C. She was a reptilian alien unable to mate with humans

# SPOT THE DIFFERENCE

# AN UNDERWATER MYSTERY

The official explanation for the *Kursk* submarine disaster, in which 118 people died, is that a faulty torpedo was to blame. Alternative theories include a collision with the seabed, an old World War Two mine, or that it was an act of deliberate sabotage.

Can you spot the five differences between the two submarine images below?

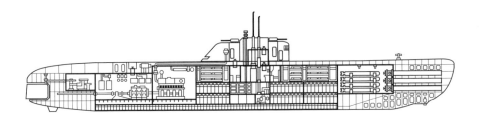

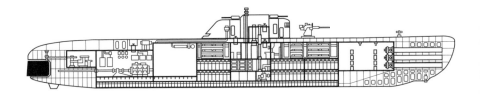

 **WORD WHEEL**

See how many words of four or more letters you can make, using each letter only once. Each word must use the central letter. Can you find the word that uses all of the letters?

Can you find the nine-letter word hidden in the grid?

| | | |
|:---:|:---:|:---:|
| L | R | P |
| T | N | I |
| E | I | A |

 **ANAGRAMS**

Rearrange these letters to reveal three things you might find inside the Earth if it were hollow.

# SCARLET NUN

_ _ _ _ _ _ _ _ _ _

# CLASSY GUNFIRE

_ _ _ _ _ _ _ _ _ _ _ _

# A NAB SIZES

_ _ _ _ _ _ _ _ _

# FLYING THE PIRATE FLAG

The Order of Skull and Bones is a secret society based at Yale University in the USA. Its past members allegedly include former presidents George W. Bush and his father George H. W. Bush. Although the group's activities are secret, rumours abound of clandestine plots to reshape the global order.

Solve the clues to find the professions taken by "Bonesmen" after leaving Yale University.

**Across**

3. Roman bigwig (7)

4. High-ranking foreign diplomat (10)

6. Diana Ross' place for tennis (7, 5)

**Down**

1. Head of a republic (9)

2. Typical (14)

5. Referee (5)

According to QAnon, who conspired against Donald Trump while he was president of the United States?

A. An alien cabal of hoax climate change profiteers

B. A secret communist order of reptilian politicians

C. A global child sex trafficking ring of satanic cannibals

# AN AIRPLANE DISASTER

On the evening of 31 May 2009, Air France Flight 447 took off from Rio de Janeiro–Galeão International Airport bound for Paris, France. It never arrived. One theory claims that the plane was zapped from the sky by a new airborne laser being tested by US military officials.

Match up the airplane symbols. The first one has been done for you.

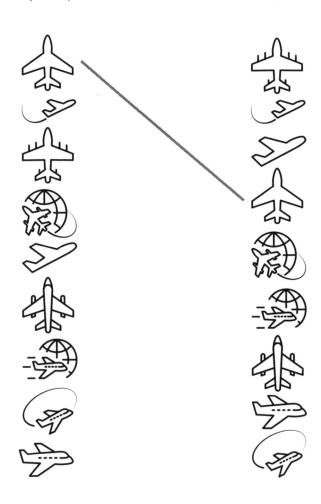

 **ACROSTICS**

Solve the clues correctly and the shaded squares will reveal a paranormal being.

1. Accompanies thunder
2. Aircraft vapour line
3. Also known as a lycanthrope
4. First man on the moon
5. Silent communication between minds

___  ___  ___  ___  ___

# GET THE REPTILIAN TO THE THRONE

According to this theory, all those in positions of power are actually shape-shifting, reptilian humanoids who aim to enslave humanity. Anyone with power or influence could be part of the reptilian elite – actors, musicians, politicians... even the British Royal Family.

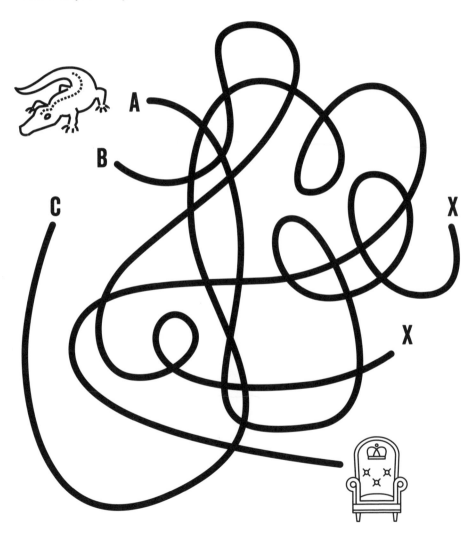

 **SUDOKU**

Complete the following grid by filling in the empty boxes with the missing numbers. Each number can only appear once in a row, column or box.

| | | 8 | 7 | 3 | | | | |
|---|---|---|---|---|---|---|---|---|
| 2 | 7 | | 5 | 9 | | | | |
| | | | 8 | 1 | 7 | | | |
| | | 2 | 9 | 7 | | 4 | 1 | 5 |
| 3 | 1 | 4 | | 6 | | 8 | 9 | |
| | 9 | | 1 | 8 | 2 | 3 | 6 | |
| | 4 | | 5 | | | | | 2 |
| 8 | 5 | 9 | 2 | | 1 | 7 | 4 | |
| 1 | 2 | 8 | | 7 | 9 | | | |

# WORDSEARCH

## IS TUPAC SHAKUR REALLY DEAD?

Tupac Shakur was pronounced dead on 13 September 1996 as a result of being shot five times after leaving the Mike Tyson fight in Las Vegas, USA. Some theorists believe that Shakur faked his death to be free of the stifling publicity that came with his high-profile outlaw lifestyle.

```
T C H G F D S A W E R M T Y U
Y R H J K L F V B N U U E R L
U E A S D F G H J H J S B N A
I M I K E T Y S O N A I S S S
O A N M H J I K L E R C S D V
S T A S D F G H J K Y V I L E
E E D F G H J K R J K I L O G
D D A S D F G U A S D D U I A
R S F G H J K F G H J E J K S
G A N G L A N D I O P O S D F
T O Q W H E R T Y Y U J K L N
Y P O S T M O R T E M Q W E R
F I A S D F R A P P E R Z X C
G I E I O U G T H Y U Y U I O
I B E S T S E L L I N G A S D
```

| BESTSELLING | LAS VEGAS | POSTMORTEM |
| CREMATED | MIKE TYSON | RAPPER |
| GANGLAND | MUSIC VIDEO | SHAKUR |

According to some theorists, what causes the aurora borealis?

A. Alien experiments at the North Pole

B. Nuclear weapons testing beneath Antarctica

C. Light shining out from another sun inside the Earth

# SPOT THE DIFFERENCE

# ALIEN ABDUCTION IN NEW HAMPSHIRE

In 1961, Barney and Betty Hill reported a time loss of two hours after spotting a UFO. In therapy, they both gave a clear description of what is now the archetypal alien depiction — big grey head with slanted eyes.

Can you spot the five differences between the two alien images below?

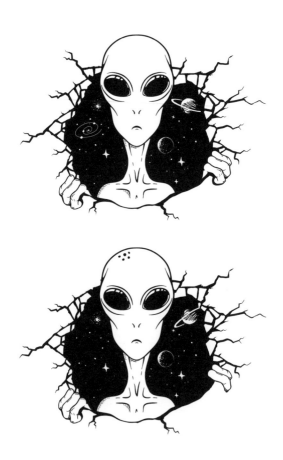

# BETWEEN THE LINES

An infamous assassin can be inserted in the blank line so that, reading downwards, six three-letter words are formed. What is the hidden word between the lines?

| R | A | A | L | E | A |
|---|---|---|---|---|---|
|   |   |   |   |   |   |
| D | K | E | D | K | D |

See how many words of four or more letters you can make, using each letter only once. Each word must use the central letter. Can you find the word that uses all of the letters?

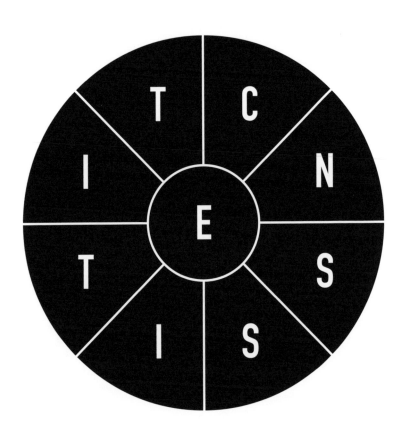

Rearrange these letters to reveal three methods of mind control.

# BANISHING WAR

_ _ _ _ _ _ _ _ _ _ _

# MINTY SHOP

_ _ _ _ _ _ _ _

# SPINDLE OPERATIVE

_ _ _ _ _ _ _ _ _ _ _ _ _ _ _ _

# ACROSTICS

**Solve the clues correctly and the shaded squares will reveal a rebellious royal.**

1. What Guy Fawkes was hiding

2. Fast-moving conflagrations

3. Mozart's middle name

4. Camouflaged

5. The Earth without a curve

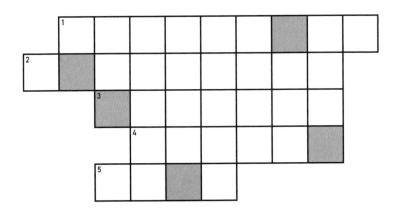

$$\text{alien} \times \text{alien} = 9$$

$$\text{alien} + \text{UFO} = 18$$

$$\text{UFO} - \text{Earth} = 8$$

$$\text{UFO} \div \text{alien} \times \text{Earth} = \text{?}$$

In 1944, the Port Chicago disaster killed hundreds of US Navy servicemen in a matter of seconds. How do some theorists account for the blast that took place?

A. A nuclear experiment gone wrong

B. A sneak attack by Japanese forces

C. A weather control experiment gone wrong

 **HIDDEN WORD**

Can you find the nine-letter word hidden in the grid?

| | | |
|---|---|---|
| R | G | T |
| M | H | L |
| A | I | O |

# THE PHANTOM TIME HYPOTHESIS

According to this theory, the year 613CE was not followed by 614. Instead, the calendar jumped straight to the year 911 in order to make the Holy Roman Emperor, Pope and Byzantine Emperor into important figures at the millennium.

Match up the time symbols. The first one has been done for you.

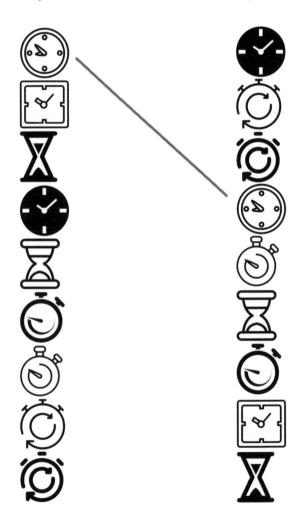

$$\text{(gas mask)} \times \text{(barrel)} = 32$$

$$\text{(skull)} + \text{(skull)} = 22$$

$$\text{(skull)} - \text{(gas mask)} = 7$$

$$\text{(gas mask)} + \text{(barrel)} - \text{(skull)} = ?$$

# CROSSWORD

# A SWEET TOOTH

While it is widely accepted to be okay in moderation, there are those who believe that sugar is a poison and that its industry has been covering up evidence of its harmful nature for decades, much in the way the tobacco lobbies did with smoking.

Solve the clues to find foods on the supermarket shelves that, perhaps surprisingly, can contain high levels of added sugar.

### Across

3. Warhol's artistic can (6, 4)
4. Legumes from the oven (5, 5)
5. Streaky swine (5)

### Down

1. Signal address (anag.) (5, 8)
2. Cultured milk (6)
4. Outside of a sandwich (5)

# GET THE DICTATOR TO THE MOON

Could Hitler have faked his own death and escaped to the moon at the end of World War Two? The Nazis had been developing sophisticated rockets for years, and some think the Führer was blasted into space to live in a secret base with up to 40,000 other colonists.

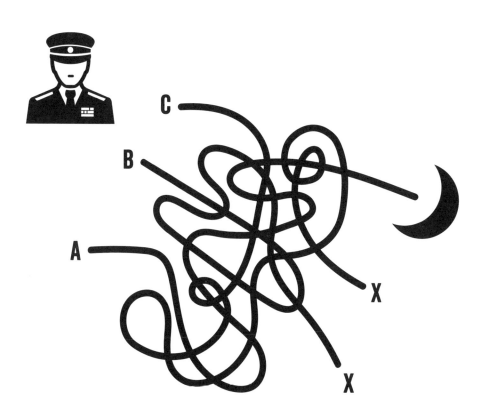

Whose father did Donald Trump link to Lee Harvey Oswald, the infamous assassin of John F. Kennedy?

A. Ron DeSantis

B. Ted Cruz

C. Joe Biden

 **WORDSEARCH**

# WAS THE BREXIT REFERENDUM RIGGED?

The "Leave" result in the 2016 referendum on whether the UK should remain in the European Union sent shockwaves around the world. Almost inevitably, it gave rise to scores of conspiracy theories, including Russian interference, voter suppression and plans by MI5 to change votes manually.

```
E  S  T  A  B  L  I  S  H  M  E  N  T  V  A
D  F  G  H  J  E  W  E  R  F  D  S  A  O  F
B  D  W  A  G  A  O  O  P  E  R  T  Y  T  A
N  F  D  C  V  V  A  S  D  F  G  H  J  I  C
H  G  T  Q  C  E  X  C  V  B  N  M  K  N  E
F  R  U  S  S  I  A  N  S  D  F  G  H  G  B
T  H  J  H  Y  U  J  I  K  O  K  J  F  B  O
U  P  R  O  P  A  G  A  N  D  A  Q  W  O  O
I  U  O  E  A  D  F  G  T  B  Y  U  I  O  K
O  T  P  I  M  G  T  Y  J  I  K  G  F  T  O
R  I  R  A  I  A  B  G  H  J  K  K  Y  H  Y
E  N  T  A  S  D  I  F  G  H  H  J  K  I  O
W  U  Y  Q  S  E  D  N  G  H  B  N  S  D  D
Q  I  U  T  Y  U  I  O  D  F  G  H  J  Y  C
S  U  P  E  R  S  T  A  T  E  Q  W  E  R  I
```

| ESTABLISHMENT | PROPAGANDA | RUSSIANS |
|---|---|---|
| FACEBOOK | PUTIN | SUPERSTATE |
| LEAVE | REMAIN | VOTING BOOTH |

# WORD WHEEL

See how many words of four or more letters you can make, using each letter only once. Each word must use the central letter. Can you find the word that uses all of the letters?

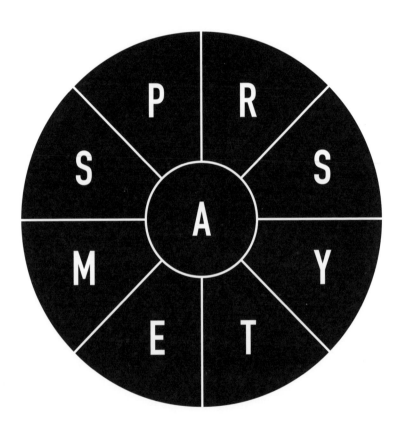

 # ACROSTICS

Solve the clues correctly and the shaded squares will reveal a dangerous virus.

1. Site of a serious meltdown
2. Flaming extraterrestrial rocks
3. Suppress the truth
4. Penetrate an organization
5. Forecast beforehand

Complete the following grid by filling in the empty boxes with the missing numbers. Each number can only appear once in a row, column or box.

|   |   |   |   |   | 8 | 3 | 4 |   |
|---|---|---|---|---|---|---|---|---|
|   |   | 5 |   | 2 | 7 |   | 8 |   |
|   | 8 |   | 4 | 3 | 5 | 6 | 7 |   |
| 8 |   | 4 | 9 | 1 |   | 2 | 3 | 7 |
|   |   | 7 | 3 | 5 |   |   |   |   |
| 6 |   | 1 | 7 | 8 | 2 | 5 | 9 |   |
| 5 | 9 | 8 | 2 |   | 3 |   | 1 | 6 |
| 4 |   | 6 | 5 | 7 | 9 |   |   |   |
| 2 | 7 | 3 |   | 6 |   | 4 |   |   |

According to flat-earthers, what causes lunar eclipses to happen?

A. An invisible anti-moon

B. A wall of ice thousands of miles high

C. An antigravity force known as "dark energy"

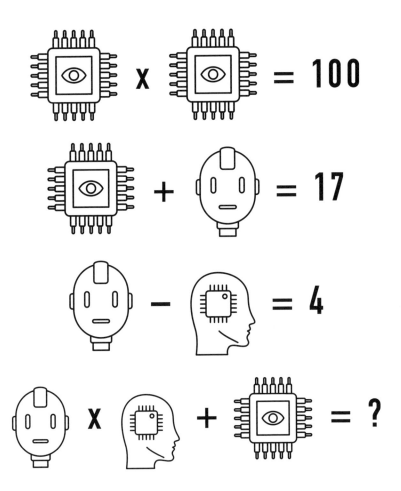

A city which has changed its official seal to reflect its importance for conspiracy theorists can be inserted in the blank line so that, reading downwards, seven three-letter words are formed. What is the hidden word between the lines?

| U | P | A | A | W | E | P |
|---|---|---|---|---|---|---|
|   |   |   |   |   |   |   |
| N | D | P | E | T | F | Y |

# SUSPICIOUS SUPERPOWERS: WHO POISONED ALEXANDER LITVINENKO?

When former Russian Federal Security Service officer Alexander Litvinenko died on 23 November 2006, the cause of death was determined as the first recorded case of polonium-210-induced acute radiation syndrome. The question of who was responsible still hangs in the air.

```
Q  D  R  F  T  G  Y  B  N  M  S  O  P  I  P
C  K  O  V  T  U  N  I  P  J  I  M  O  F  L
V  S  W  Q  F  G  D  O  J  A  Q  W  L  D  I
B  D  L  U  G  O  V  I  K  D  F  G  O  H  T
N  F  F  A  S  D  F  A  S  D  F  B  N  I  V
S  A  L  I  S  B  U  R  Y  I  Y  L  I  N  I
G  R  D  S  D  F  G  H  J  K  L  O  U  S  N
H  T  F  A  S  D  F  G  S  J  K  L  M  L  E
J  Y  G  W  D  C  V  V  H  J  K  L  L  T  N
K  U  H  G  H  L  O  N  D  O  N  N  M  C  K
E  I  J  A  S  Z  E  F  G  Y  H  U  J  I  O
R  O  R  Q  E  S  S  I  A  F  G  H  J  S  S
T  P  W  R  U  S  S  I  A  S  C  J  I  O  P
A  H  E  S  D  F  G  H  J  K  I  K  O  F  G
Q  B  I  L  L  I  O  N  A  I  R  E  A  S  D
```

| | | |
|---|---|---|
| BILLIONAIRE | LITVINENKO | POLONIUM |
| BEREZOVSKY | LONDON | RUSSIA |
| KOVTUN | LUGOVI | SALISBURY |

# IS THIS A SCRIBE I SEE BEFORE ME?

Is Shakespeare history's greatest literary hoax? There are those who believe that the classics credited to him were not actually written by Stratford-upon-Avon's most famous son. Candidates for the real author of works such as *Othello* and *The Merchant of Venice* include dramatist Christopher Marlowe, philosopher Sir Francis Bacon and Queen Elizabeth I.

Can you spot the five differences between the two images of Shakespeare below?

Rearrange these letters to reveal three ways to spread conspiracies…

# AI INFORMS MONTI

_ _ _ _ _ _ _ _ _ _ _ _ _ _

# ASKEW FEN

_ _ _ _ _ _ _ _

# DRAGON PAPA

_ _ _ _ _ _ _ _ _ _

 **CROSSWORD**

# A SURPRISE ATTACK

One of the defining moments of World War Two was the Japanese attack on Pearl Harbor, which brought the US into the war. But was the attack in December 1941 really a surprise? Theorists believe that then president Franklin D. Roosevelt knew about the planned attack and kept it secret to promote his wartime ambitions.

Solve the clues to discover what was at Pearl Harbor that day.

**Across**

2. Attack from above (3, 4)
5. A bellybutton, quickly (5, 5)
6. Seafaring butterfly (7)

**Down**

1. Berth place of a boat (8)
3. Fighting boat (10)
4. Roystered (anag.) (9)

# FIRE IN THE SKY

In 2013, the world was shocked by footage of a huge meteor descending toward Russia and exploding in a massive ball of flame over the Chelyabinsk region. Theorists have speculated that the meteor story was a cover for weapons tests or the precursor to an alien invasion.

Match up the meteor symbols. The first one has been done for you.

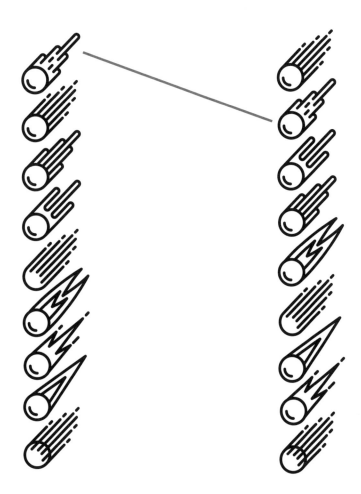

# ALIEN BIG CATS

Many people claim to have spotted a gigantic beast roaming the wilds, its shadow recognizable as a cat of unnatural proportions. Some believe that the cats are hybrids of abandoned zoo and circus big cats bred with indigenous species, producing new creatures of abnormal size and form.

Can you spot the five differences between the two alien big cat images below?

# GET THE ROCK STAR TO THE TARGET

There are numerous conspiracy theories surrounding Elvis Presley, not least that he faked his own death and has been seen working in a burger bar. Another theory speculates that Elvis may have killed former US president John F. Kennedy for hogging the media coverage.

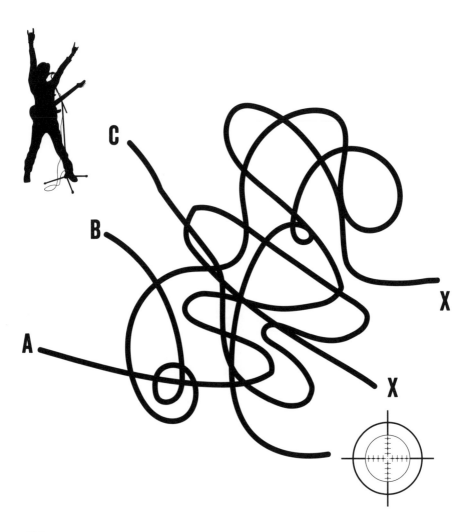

Can you find the nine-letter word hidden in the grid?

| | | |
|:-:|:-:|:-:|
| B | E | I |
| N | I | V |
| I | S | L |

The debunked 2016 conspiracy theory, Pizzagate, claimed that which high-ranking politician was leading a child abuse ring from a Washington pizzeria?

A. Bill Clinton

B. Hillary Clinton

C. Barack Obama

 **WORDSEARCH**

# WAS MOZART MURDERED?

Conspiracy theories sprang up immediately after Mozart's death in 1791 at the age of 35. One theory suggests that his arch-rival Antonio Salieri killed him, while others point the finger at the Freemasons, claiming that Mozart planned to establish a rival order.

```
C O M P O S E R Q W E R T T F
R R A U F V G B H N O Y U I R
Q A G A S B G R D S R T G Y E
B G I S S I O O P V C E I T E
O O C V D E C W S E H E D F M
A S F E D R F J K L E I O P A
S D L G H J W N B Y S F G H S
E R U G H Y O F G H T R G Y O
Y H T O S I L O O P R Z A Q N
O P E R A Q F S D F A O P I S
A E R T L H G U J U U O P B N
W F T Y I U A V I E N N A O I
F G H S E A N E C R V T N U I
A H R Q R S G E R T Y U I O B
H J R T I D E R F T G Y H U H
```

| | | |
|---|---|---|
| COMPOSER | MUSIC | SALIERI |
| FREEMASONS | OPERA | VIENNA |
| MAGIC FLUTE | ORCHESTRA | WOLFGANG |

# WILDFIRES IN CALIFORNIA

Were California's 2018 wildfires deliberately started by a secret cabal of influential billionaires using directed energy weapons? Proponents of the theory claim that "light pillars" from the sky were seen targeting rural homes, igniting fires hotter and spreading faster than nature could ever produce.

Match up the advanced weapon symbols. The first one has been done for you.

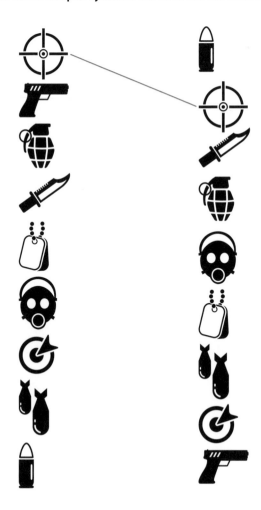

$$\text{(virus A)} \div \text{(microbe B)} = 6$$

$$\text{(microbe B)} \times \text{(virus C)} = 21$$

$$\text{(virus D)} \times \text{(virus E)} = 36$$

$$\text{(microbe B)} + \text{(virus C)} + \text{(virus E)} = \; ?$$

# CROSSWORD

# ART FOR THE GODS

The Nazca Lines have been a source of fascination for centuries. They appear in the Nazca Desert high in the Peruvian Andes and resemble drawings of all sorts of animals, as well as simple geometric patterns, shapes and straight lines. Mysteriously, many of the drawings are indistinguishable on the ground and can only be appreciated from the air.

Solve the clues to find the creatures depicted by the Nazca Lines.

**Across**

1. Angler's quarry (4)

3. Cheeky children (7)

5. Geckos you might find in a lounge (7)

6. Hitchcock's 1963 movie (5)

**Down**

2. You and me (6)

4. Web designers (7)

Some theorists believe that HAARP is a secret *Star Wars*-era weapon employed by the US government to influence domestic and foreign affairs. What does the acronym HAARP stand for?

A. High-frequency Active Auroral Research Program

B. High Alert Acoustic Responder Program

C. High Altitude Alien Reconnaissance Program

# SHUTTLE DISASTER

When the NASA space shuttle *Columbia* exploded upon re-entry in February 2003, some theorized that it wasn't an accident. The main curiosity centred on a link to the Arab–Israeli conflict in the Middle East. The first debris from the disintegrating aircraft was found in the town of Palestine, Texas, USA. Coincidence or something far more disquieting?

Can you spot the five differences between the two space shuttle images below?

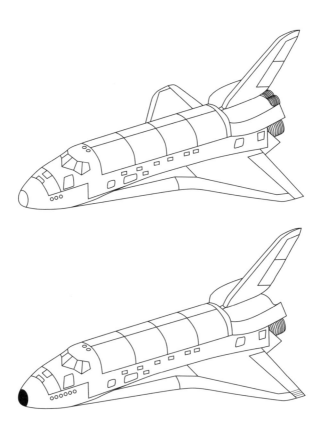

 **MAZE**

# GET GRETA TO THE TIME MACHINE

Is Greta Thunberg a time traveller? Proponents of this unusual theory point to a photo of a girl who bears an uncanny resemblance to the acclaimed climate activist, taken around 1898 and showing three children working at a gold mine in Canada. One of them is a girl with Thunberg's braided hairdo and stern expression.

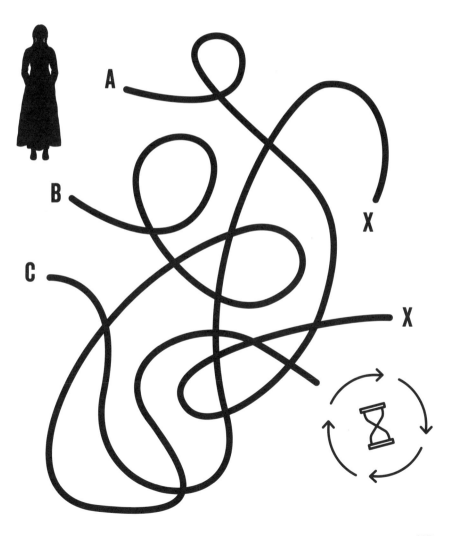

# ANSWERS

**1:** 1. THE MOON, 2. ARGENTINA, 3. ROCKET, 4. BODY DOUBLES, 5. ANTARTICA, 6. UBOAT

**2:**

**3:**

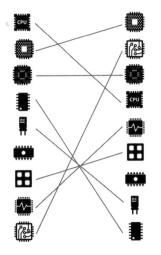

**4:** A – he'd been killed several years before

**5:**

| J | A | L | I | E | N | H | Y | B | R | I | D | D | D | O |
|---|---|---|---|---|---|---|---|---|---|---|---|---|---|---|
| D | I | A | J | A | U | Z | X | C | V | B | A | N | M | N |
| E | L | A | J | T | I | J | U | I | O | P | V | Q | Q | E |
| R | L | Z | L | A | O | H | H | J | K | K | I | N | C | W |
| H | U | M | A | N | B | L | O | O | D | B | D | O | L | O |
| T | M | G | O | Q | Q | B | U | N | H | S | I | D | D | R |
| Y | I | G | O | W | W | H | J | K | C | V | C | W | N | L |
| U | N | H | P | E | E | Q | A | S | C | V | K | M | M | D |
| I | A | J | Q | R | R | Q | W | E | R | T | E | J | J | S |
| H | T | K | Q | T | T | L | V | V | X | S | I | I | K | T |
| F | I | L | R | E | P | T | I | L | I | A | N | A | S | A |
| P | R | I | N | C | E | P | H | I | L | I | P | K | K | T |
| X |   | R | S | B | B | S | A | E | E | E | Q | U | Y | E |
| T | O | T | A | L | I | T | A | R | I | A | N | L | O | P |
| C | M | O | U | N | T | B | A | T | T | E | N | P | O | N |

**6:** (🐢 = 7, 🦅 = 13, 🐍 = 3);
13 x 3 - 7 = 32

**7:** B

**8:** Finland

**9:** B – George W. Bush

**10:** Freemason

**11:**

| 6 | 1 | 8 | 4 | 7 | 9 | 3 | 2 | 5 |
|---|---|---|---|---|---|---|---|---|
| 5 | 7 | 4 | 3 | 2 | 6 | 9 | 1 | 8 |
| 2 | 3 | 9 | 1 | 5 | 8 | 4 | 6 | 7 |
| 3 | 4 | 1 | 7 | 9 | 2 | 5 | 8 | 6 |
| 9 | 5 | 7 | 8 | 6 | 3 | 1 | 4 | 2 |
| 8 | 2 | 6 | 5 | 4 | 1 | 7 | 9 | 3 |
| 1 | 9 | 5 | 2 | 8 | 7 | 6 | 3 | 4 |
| 4 | 6 | 2 | 9 | 3 | 5 | 8 | 7 | 1 |
| 7 | 8 | 3 | 6 | 1 | 4 | 2 | 5 | 9 |

12: terrorist, helicopter, debunk, towers, phantom = TRUTH

13: Kurt Cobain, Elvis Presley, Michael Jackson

14:

| C | A | R | P | E | N | T | E | R | E | E | R | T | Y | B |
|---|---|---|---|---|---|---|---|---|---|---|---|---|---|---|
| A | A | S | V | C | H | R | I | S | T | I | A | N | M | L |
| M | P | Q | E | R | T | U | G | D | F | C | A | A | C | O |
| M | I | O | A | A | M | S | D | F | I | R | A | R | R | O |
| A | H | H | S | D | F | L | I | E | R | U | V | B | J | D |
| G | A | S | D | T | W | D | B | N | N | C | A | S | D | L |
| D | J | H | G | F | L | E | E | O | I | I | D | D | K | I |
| A | Q | W | E | R | E | E | T | Y | U | F | I | O | K | N |
| L | A | S | D | F | O | H | J | K | L | I | B | B | C | E |
| E | S | S | U | I | N | S | S | D | L | X | K | K | K | O |
| N | Y | T | R | W | A | Q | Q | Q | S | I | X | X | U | Y |
| E | A | S | P | R | I | O | R | Y | O | F | S | I | O | N |
| H | J | K | O | U | D | Q | Q | B | B | N | J | K | L | M |
| J | J | I | O | H | O | L | Y | G | R | A | I | L | W | E |
| T | Y | U | I | G | F | D | S | A | K | L | E | E | R | S |

15: nine-letter word = biohazard; other words = hairdo, hazard, abhor, dhobi, hoard, haar, hair, hard, hoar, hora

16:

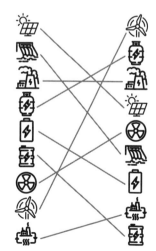

17: A – in his palms

18: 1. OVERPOPULATION, 2. LABORATORY, 3. TARGETED, 4. ACCIDENT, 5. MANMADE, 6. BIOWEAPON

19: nine-letter word = espionage; other words = epigones, agonies, agonise, apogees, epigone, peonage, peonies, pigeons, seeping, soignee, apogee, easing, genies, genips, opines, peeing, pigeon, pongee, ponies, seeing, senega, soigne, sponge, aegis, aeons, agone, anise, aspen, eosin, gapes, geans, genes, genie, genip, genoa, napes, neaps, noise, opens, opine, paeon, pages, panes, peags, peans, pease, peens, peons, pines, poise, pones, segno, seine, sepia, siege, singe, snipe, spine, aeon, ages, apes, apse, ease, egos, eons, epos, gape, gean, gees, gene, gens, goes, gone, nape, neap, noes, nope, nose, ogee, ones, open, page, pane, peag, pean, peas, peen, pees, pegs, pein, peng, pens, peon, peso, pies, pine, pone, pose, sage, sane, seen, seep, sene, sine, sone, spae

20:

21: A

22: chemtrails

23: abductees

**24:** Freemasons, Illuminati, New World Order

**25:** (  = 10, = 3, = 7);
$3 \times 7 - 10 = 11$

**26:** 1. BRAINWASHING,
2. ELECTROSHOCK, 3. HEROIN,
4. HYPNOSIS, 5. LSD,
6. MARIJUANA

**27:** unsinkable, virus, theorize, space, knight = KURSK

**28:** B

**29:**

**30:** nine-letter word = brainwash; other words = bashaw, wasabi, awash, brawn, bwana, nawab, swain, wains, warns, whins, whirs, awns, braw, haws, sawn, shaw, shwa, swab, swan, wain, warn, wars, wash, whin, whir, wins, wish

**31:** echelon

**32:**

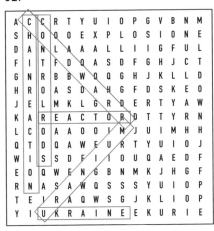

| A | C | C | R | T | Y | U | I | O | P | G | V | B | N | M |
|---|---|---|---|---|---|---|---|---|---|---|---|---|---|---|
| S | H | O | Q | O | E | X | P | L | O | S | I | O | N | E |
| D | A | N | L | A | A | A | L | L | I | I | G | F | U | L |
| F | I | T | F | D | Q | A | S | D | F | G | H | J | C | T |
| G | N | R | B | B | W | Q | G | H | J | K | L | L | D |   |
| H | R | O | A | S | D | A | H | G | F | D | S | K | E | O |
| J | E | L | M | K | L | G | R | D | E | R | T | Y | A | W |
| K | A | R | E | A | C | T | O | R | D | T | T | Y | R | N |
| L | C | O | A | A | O | O | I | M | J | U | I | M | H | H |
| Q | T | D | Q | A | W | E | U | R | T | Y | U | I | O | J |
| W | I | S | S | D | F | I | I | O | U | Q | A | E | D | F |
| E | O | Q | W | E | N | G | B | N | M | K | J | H | G | F |
| R | N | A | S | A | W | Q | S | S | S | Y | U | I | O | P |
| T | E | I | R | A | Q | W | S | G | J | K | L | I | O | P |
| Y | I | U | K | R | A | I | N | E | E | K | U | R | I | E |

**33:** believers

**34:** ( = 4 = 9 = 13);
$9 \times 13 - 4 = 113$

**35:** cabal, Atlantic, tornado, microchip, kidnapped = BLACK

**36:** A – immediately before the Twin Towers collapsed

**37:**

| 1 | 2 | 7 | 3 | 9 | 6 | 4 | 8 | 5 |
|---|---|---|---|---|---|---|---|---|
| 5 | 6 | 8 | 1 | 4 | 2 | 9 | 7 | 3 |
| 4 | 9 | 3 | 5 | 8 | 7 | 2 | 1 | 6 |
| 9 | 5 | 6 | 2 | 3 | 8 | 1 | 4 | 7 |
| 7 | 8 | 2 | 6 | 1 | 4 | 3 | 5 | 9 |
| 3 | 1 | 4 | 9 | 7 | 5 | 6 | 2 | 8 |
| 6 | 7 | 1 | 4 | 5 | 3 | 8 | 9 | 2 |
| 8 | 3 | 9 | 7 | 2 | 1 | 5 | 6 | 4 |
| 2 | 4 | 5 | 8 | 6 | 9 | 7 | 3 | 1 |

**38:** extraterrestrial, martian, venusian

**39:**

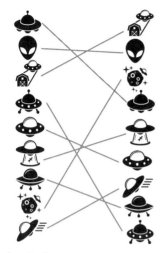

**40:** bacterium

**41:** B

**42:** ($\bigwedge\bigwedge\bigwedge$ = 2   🦆 = 7   ▲ = 20);
$20 \div 2 - 7 = 3$

**43:** fluoride

**44:**

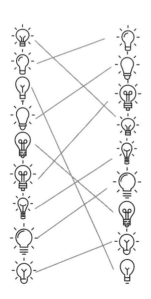

**45:**

| | | | | | | | | | | | | | |
|---|---|---|---|---|---|---|---|---|---|---|---|---|---|
| C | L | I | M | A | T | E | A | S | Q | V | B | W | J | J |
| A | D | A | Q | A | Q | N | S | A | A | O | Q | I | Q | G |
| D | S | S | A | S | A | V | T | P | Q | Z | A | N | W | R |
| F | A | H | Z | D | S | I | Y | A | F | O | S | D | E | E |
| G | S | J | Z | F | D | R | U | R | G | N | D | P | R | E |
| H | D | K | F | G | F | O | I | I | H | E | F | O | T | N |
| J | F | L | E | H | G | N | O | S | J | Q | G | W | Y | H |
| K | G | V | D | J | H | M | P | A | K | A | H | E | U | O |
| K | K | B | T | K | J | E | P | S | L | S | J | R | I | U |
| L | I | N | H | L | K | N | X | H | P | X | K | S | O | S |
| I | O | M | J | I | L | T | F | T | Q | F | O | V | A | E |
| O | P | L | I | I | O | D | G | I | R | G | I | H | S | A |
| P | K | Y | O | T | O | S | H | O | E | E | U | I | D | A |
| R | R | R | K | O | O | I | J | P | R | J | M | Q | F | A |
| S | R | U | L | F | O | S | S | I | L | F | U | E | L | A |

**46:** B – nuclear bomb

**47:** conspiracy, metal, Jupiter, Roswell, supernatural = ALIEN

**48:** nine-letter word = wildfires; other words = wildfire, felids, fields, filers, fliers, lifers, rifled, rifles, felid, field, filed, filer, files, fired, fires, flews, flied, flier, flies, fried, fries, lifer, rifle, serif, feds, file, fils, fire, firs, fled, flew, lief, life, refs, rife, self, serf, wife, wifi

**49:** kidnapped

**50:** 1. ASTRONAUT, 2. GRAVITY, 3. SATELLITE, 4. MOONLANDING, 5. GALAXIES, 6. PLANETS

**51:**

| | | | | | | | | |
|---|---|---|---|---|---|---|---|---|
| 6 | 4 | 2 | 1 | 7 | 8 | 5 | 3 | 9 |
| 3 | 7 | 9 | 6 | 4 | 5 | 2 | 8 | 1 |
| 1 | 8 | 5 | 2 | 9 | 3 | 4 | 6 | 7 |
| 2 | 5 | 8 | 9 | 1 | 4 | 6 | 7 | 3 |
| 4 | 3 | 7 | 5 | 8 | 6 | 1 | 9 | 2 |
| 9 | 6 | 1 | 3 | 2 | 7 | 8 | 5 | 4 |
| 5 | 9 | 3 | 4 | 6 | 2 | 7 | 1 | 8 |
| 7 | 1 | 4 | 8 | 5 | 9 | 3 | 2 | 6 |
| 8 | 2 | 6 | 7 | 3 | 1 | 9 | 4 | 5 |

**52:** car bomb, telescopic rifle, lethal injection

**53:** Illuminati

**54:** nine-letter word = carcasses; other words = carcass, access, arecas, Caesar, caress, scarce, scares, acres, areca, caeca, cares, carse, cases, crass, cress, races, sacra, scare, scars, aces, acre, arcs, care, cars, casa, case, ceca, cess, race, sacs, scar, secs

**55:** B

**56:** vaccinate, blast-off, Clinton, simulation, disappear = EBOLA

**57:** B – a computer game manifesting in real life

**58:** 1. LIFEBOATS, 2. CAPTAIN, 3. UNSINKABLE, 4. PASSENGERS, 5. MAIDEN VOYAGE, 6. ATLANTIC

**59:**

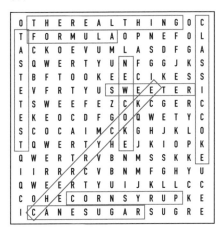

**60:**

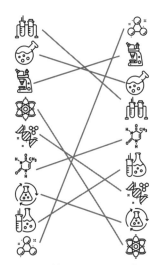

**61:** ( = 2, = 3, = 4); 4 + 2 − 3 = 3

**62:** telepathy, telekinesis, precognition

63:

64: C – he is secretly an Islamic
extremist

65: B

66: vaccine

67:

68: C – to keep private prisons full

69: ($\heartsuit$ = 5, 💊 = 1, 💉 = 19);
19 + 1 − 5 = 15

70: microchip

71: social networks, smartphones,
credit cards

72:

73:

| 8 | 2 | 6 | 7 | 9 | 4 | 3 | 5 | 1 |
| 9 | 3 | 7 | 6 | 1 | 5 | 8 | 4 | 2 |
| 5 | 1 | 4 | 3 | 8 | 2 | 9 | 7 | 6 |
| 4 | 5 | 2 | 9 | 3 | 6 | 1 | 8 | 7 |
| 7 | 8 | 3 | 5 | 4 | 1 | 2 | 6 | 9 |
| 6 | 9 | 1 | 2 | 7 | 8 | 4 | 3 | 5 |
| 3 | 4 | 5 | 1 | 2 | 7 | 6 | 9 | 8 |
| 1 | 7 | 9 | 8 | 6 | 3 | 5 | 2 | 4 |
| 2 | 6 | 8 | 4 | 5 | 9 | 7 | 1 | 3 |

74: priest, vacuum, attack,
investigate, needle = PUTIN

**75:**

```
S Q W E R T Y U O H P P T G G
E C S G Y H U J I O W S D E R
N O I U S D F G H N Z X C V E
S A S D F G T H N G Z X F T E
E G H J K L U Y I K A Q W E N
I A G H J K L W O O Q A S D H
J K U N G F U O O N A G H H O
R T Y U I V B F G G A K L L R
T P R E S S U R E P O I N T N
B R U C E L E E X C C J I K E
A S D N J I O P E D F G R E T
M A R T I A L A R T S A Z C F
A S D F D M O V I E S T A R Q
Q A S D F G H H Y U I O T N H
W A C T I O N H E R O W W W W
```

**76:** nine-letter word = chemicals;
other words = alchemic,
chemical, chasmic, camels,
camise, chimes, claims, climes,
emails, haemic, hiemal, malice,
mascle, mashie, meccas,
mescal, mesial, sachem,
samiel, schema, acmes, amice,
calms, camel, chasm, chime,
claim, clams, clime, email,
hames, helms, lames, limes,
maces, macle, mails, males,
meals, mecca, melic, mesic,
milch, miles, salmi, shame,
slime, smile, acme, ahem, aims,
alms, amie, calm, came, cams,
cham, clam, clem, elms, haem,
hame, hams, helm, hems, lame,
lams, lime, mace, macs, mail,
male, mash, meal, mesa, mesh,
mica, mice, mics, mile, mils,
mise, same, scam, seam, semi,
sham, shim, sima, slam, slim

**77:** Lennon

**78:** Osama bin Laden, Martin
Luther King, John F. Kennedy

**79:**

**80:** C

**81:** A – to help Vladimir Putin
become president

**82:** ( $\boxed{\text{💵}}$ = 9 $\boxed{\text{💰}}$ = 1 $\boxed{\text{🪙}}$ = 1);
1 x 1 x 9 = 9

**83:**

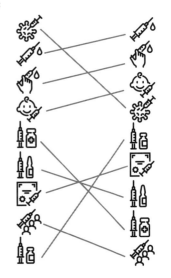

84: nine-letter word = deception; other words = entopic, epidote, pentode, pointed, potence; six-letter words: copied, depict, depone, incept, opened, opined, pecten, pectin, pieced, poetic, ponced, ponied, poteen, coped, depot, epode, inept, opine, opted, optic, pence, picot, piece, pined, pinto, piton, point, ponce, tepid, toped, topee, topic, cope, deep, dope, epic, nope, oped, open, peed, peen, pein, pent, peon, pice, pied, piet, pine, pint, pion, poet, pond, pone, tope, topi

85: communist, Katrina, warfare, Bigfoot, Apollo = MAFIA

86: (⊕ = 1  🛑 = 9  🔫 = 14);
14 + 9 − 1 = 22

87: debunking

88: moon landing

89:

| W | C | L | O | U | D | S | E | E | D | I | N | G | W | P |
|---|---|---|---|---|---|---|---|---|---|---|---|---|---|---|
| E | O | U | Q | W | E | R | T | E | D | F | G | H | L | R |
| A | P | N | M | T | E | Q | I | X | Q | Q | Y | J | Y | O |
| T | R | N | E | L | I | A | O | P | W | A | Y | H | N | J |
| H | E | N | T | F | O | E | I | E | E | Z | U | G | M | E |
| E | C | N | E | G | S | N | I | R | R | X | I | F | O | C |
| R | I | N | O | H | T | F | I | T | D | O | D | U | T | T |
| C | P | N | R | J | H | G | E | M | Y | V | P | S | T | C |
| O | I | Y | O | K | J | H | R | E | B | G | Q | A | H | U |
| N | T | T | L | O | K | J | T | N | U | U | W | L | U | M |
| T | A | R | O | O | L | K | Y | T | N | H | S | O | R | U |
| R | T | E | G | P | M | L | U | L | N | J | E | P | T | L |
| O | I | O | Y | Q | A | L | U | I | I | K | B | U | I | U |
| L | O | S | I | L | V | E | R | I | O | D | I | D | E | S |
| O | N | C | U | M | U | L | O | N | I | M | B | U | S | N |

90:

91: 1. HOUSEKEEPER, 2. ALIENS,
3. KENEDY, 4. MAFIA,
5. FREEMASONS, 6. DOCTOR

92: B

93:

| O | I | D | A | S | D | F | Y | U | O | S | X | X | I | T |
|---|---|---|---|---|---|---|---|---|---|---|---|---|---|---|
| O | V | E | R | P | O | P | U | L | A | T | I | O | N | O |
| A | S | P | C | T | Y | U | I | O | O | P | T | R | E | R |
| P | N | R | W | O | I | O | P | I | O | O | W | E | C | N |
| R | J | E | E | S | N | Q | W | D | F | G | E | J | K | A |
| E | I | S | R | E | N | O | Y | O | R | O | L | Q | Q | D |
| S | B | S | F | D | N | Q | M | P | D | O | F | Z | X | O |
| I | G | I | G | F | I | W | W | F | S | A | A | Y | E | S |
| D | D | O | H | G | U | E | E | Q | T | T | R | W | H | S |
| E | E | N | J | H | P | R | R | W | G | H | E | S | J | Q |
| N | Y | D | K | J | O | T | T | E | Y | I | I | E | U | S |
| T | U | R | O | O | S | E | V | E | L | T | I | D | U | W |
| E | I | O | D | K | Y | Y | U | I | I | L | U | R | U | D |
| D | O | T | R | A | I | L | E | R | P | A | R | K | U | F |
| S | T | O | C | K | M | A | R | K | E | T | R | Y | P | I |

94: B – she was a man pretending to be Elizabeth

153

95:

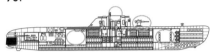

96: nine-letter word: earthling, haltering, lathering; other words = alerting, altering, atheling, earthing, ingather, integral, litharge, narghile, relating, thirlage, triangle; seven-letter words: aligner, alright, atingle, elating, engrail, gahnite, gelatin, genital, granite, halting, healing, hearing, heating, ingrate, lathing, lighten, lighter, realign, relight, ringlet, tagline, tangier, tearing, tingler, aiglet, aigret, alight, angler, argent, aright, earing, eating, gainer, gaiter, garnet, gather, genial, gratin, haling, hanger, haring, hating, hegira, ingate, length, ligate, linage, linger, nigher, rating, regain, regnal, rehang, tangle, taring, tergal, tingle, triage, agent, agile, aglet, algin, align, angel, anger, angle, argil, eight, garth, gerah, giant, girth, glair, glare, glean, glint, gnarl, grail, grain, grant, grate, great, grith, hinge, ingle, lager, large, legit, ligan, liger, light, neigh, night, range, regal, reign, right, targe, thegn, thing, tiger, tinge. gain, gait, gale, gate, gean, gear, gelt, gent, ghat, gilt, girl, girt, gite, glen, glia, gnat, gran, grin, grit, hang, nigh, rage, ragi, rang, ring, tang, ting, trig

97: reptilian

98: central sun, flying saucers, Nazi bases

99: 1. PRESIDENT,
2. REPRESENTATIVE,
3. SENATOR, 4. AMBASSADOR,
5. JUDGE, 6. SUPREME COURT

100: C – a global child sex trafficking ring of satanic cannibals

101:

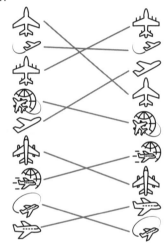

102: lightning, chemtrail, werewolf, Armstrong, telepathy = GHOST

103: C

104:

| 9 | 6 | 8 | 7 | 3 | 2 | 5 | 4 | 1 |
|---|---|---|---|---|---|---|---|---|
| 2 | 7 | 1 | 5 | 9 | 4 | 3 | 6 | 8 |
| 4 | 3 | 5 | 6 | 8 | 1 | 7 | 2 | 9 |
| 6 | 8 | 2 | 9 | 7 | 3 | 4 | 1 | 5 |
| 3 | 1 | 4 | 2 | 6 | 5 | 8 | 9 | 7 |
| 5 | 9 | 7 | 4 | 1 | 8 | 2 | 3 | 6 |
| 7 | 4 | 3 | 1 | 5 | 9 | 6 | 8 | 2 |
| 8 | 5 | 9 | 3 | 2 | 6 | 1 | 7 | 4 |
| 1 | 2 | 6 | 8 | 4 | 7 | 9 | 5 | 3 |

**105:**

| T | C | H | G | F | D | S | A | W | E | R | M | T | Y | U |
|---|---|---|---|---|---|---|---|---|---|---|---|---|---|---|
| Y | R | H | J | K | L | F | V | B | N | U | U | E | R | L |
| U | E | A | S | D | F | G | H | J | H | J | S | B | N | A |
| I | M | I | K | E | T | Y | S | O | N | A | I | S | S | S |
| O | A | N | M | H | J | I | K | L | E | R | C | S | D | V |
| S | T | A | S | D | F | G | H | J | K | Y | V | I | L | E |
| E | E | D | F | G | H | J | K | R | J | K | I | L | O | G |
| D | D | A | S | D | F | G | U | A | S | D | D | U | I | A |
| R | S | F | G | H | J | K | F | G | H | J | E | J | K | S |
| G | A | N | G | L | A | N | D | I | O | P | O | S | D | F |
| T | O | Q | W | H | E | R | T | Y | Y | U | J | K | L | N |
| Y | P | O | S | T | M | O | R | T | E | M | Q | W | E | R |
| F | I | A | S | D | F | R | A | P | P | E | R | Z | X | C |
| G | I | E | I | O | U | G | T | H | Y | U | Y | U | I | O |
| I | B | E | S | T | S | E | L | L | I | N | G | A | S | D |

**106:** C – light shining out from another sun inside the Earth

**107:**

**108:** Oswald

**109:** nine-letter word = scientist; other words = iciness, incises, incites, insects, tiniest; six-letter words: cities, iciest, incest, incise, insect, insets, insist, nicest, niseis, scents, seisin, seniti, steins, stents, stints, testis, tincts, cents, cites, inset, intis, issei, nests, nisei, scent, sects, setts, since, sines, sites, snits, stein, stent, stets, sties, stint, tents, tests, tines, tints, titis; four-letter words: cess, cist, ices, ness, nest, nets, nisi, nits, secs, sect, sent, sets, sett, sics, sine, sins, site, sits, snit, stet, tens, test, tics, ties, tins, tits

**110:** brainwashing, hypnotism, sleep deprivation

**111:** gunpowder, wildfires, Amadeus, hidden, flat = DIANA

**112:** ($\bigodot$ = 3 $\ominus$ = 15 $\oplus$ = 7); 15 ÷ 3 x 7 = 35

**113:** A – a nuclear experiment gone wrong

**114:** algorithm

**115:**

**116:** ($\odot$ = 11 $\triangle$ = 8 $\otimes$ = 4); 4 + 8 – 11 = 1

**117:** 1. SALAD DRESSING, 2. YOGURT, 3. TOMATO SOUP, 4. BAKED BEANS, 5. BACON

**118:** A

119: B – Ted Cruz

120:

```
E S T A B L I S H M E N T V A
D F G H J E W E R F D S A O F
B D W A G A O O P E R T Y T A
N F D C V V A S D F G H J I C
H G T Q C E X C V B N M K N E
F R U S S I A N S D F G H G B
T H J H Y U J I K O K J F B O
U P R O P A G A N D A Q W O O
I U O E A D F G T B Y U I O K
O T P I M G T Y J I K G F T O
R I R A I A B G H J K K Y H Y
E N T A S D I F G H H J K I O
W U Y Q S E D N G H B N S D D
Q I U T Y U I O D F G H J Y C
S U P E R S T A T E Q W E R I
```

121: nine-letter word = spymaster;
other words = mastery,
pessary, spryest, stayers,
streamy; six-letter words:
estray, mateys, mayest, pastry,
payers, repays, satyrs, smarty,
smeary, sprays, stayer,
steamy, strays, system, yeasts,
apery, artsy, empty, essay,
eyras, massy, matey, mayst,
meaty, messy, party, pasty,
patsy, payer, peaty, pesty,
prays, preys, pyres, raspy,
repay, samey, satyr, sayer,
seamy, spays, spray, stays,
stray, styes, teary, trays, treys,
tryma, types, tyres, years,
yeast, aery, army, arty, ayes,
easy, espy, eyas, eyra, pays,
pray, prey, pyre, rays, ryas,
says, spay, spry, stay, stye,
tray, trey, type, tyre, yams,
yaps, yare, year, yeas, yeps,
yest

122: Chernobyl, meteors, cover-up,
infiltrate, predict = COVID

123:

| 7 | 6 | 2 | 1 | 9 | 8 | 3 | 4 | 5 |
|---|---|---|---|---|---|---|---|---|
| 3 | 4 | 5 | 6 | 2 | 7 | 9 | 8 | 1 |
| 1 | 8 | 9 | 4 | 3 | 5 | 6 | 7 | 2 |
| 8 | 5 | 4 | 9 | 1 | 6 | 2 | 3 | 7 |
| 9 | 2 | 7 | 3 | 5 | 4 | 1 | 6 | 8 |
| 6 | 3 | 1 | 7 | 8 | 2 | 5 | 9 | 4 |
| 5 | 9 | 8 | 2 | 4 | 3 | 7 | 1 | 6 |
| 4 | 1 | 6 | 5 | 7 | 9 | 8 | 2 | 3 |
| 2 | 7 | 3 | 8 | 6 | 1 | 4 | 5 | 9 |

124: A – an invisible anti-moon

125: ( 🖥️ = 10, 🔌 = 7, 🗣️ = 3);
7 x 3 + 10 = 31

126: Roswell

127:

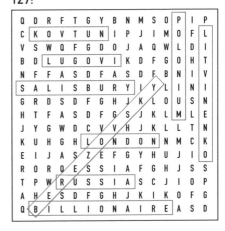

```
Q D R F T G Y B N M S O P I P
C K O V T U N I P J I M O F L
V S W Q F G D O J A Q W L D I
B D L U G O V I K D F G O H T
N F F A S D F A S D F B N I V
S A L I S B U R Y Y Y L I N I
G R D S D F G H J K L O U S N
H T F A S D F G S J K L M L E
J Y G W D C V H J K L L T N
K U H G H L O N D O N N M C K
E I J A S Z E F G Y H U J I O
R O R O E S S I A F G H J S S
T P W R U S S I A S C J I O P
A H E S D F G H J K I K O F G
Q B I L L I O N A I R E A S D
```

**128:**

**129:** misinformation, fake news, propaganda

**130:** 1. SHIPYARD, 2. AIRRAID, 3. BATTLESHIP, 4. DESTROYER, 5. NAVALFLEET, 6. ADMIRAL

**131:**

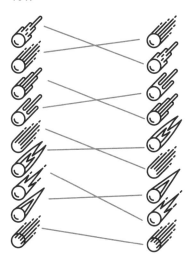

**132:**

**133:** B

**134:** invisible

**135:** B – Hillary Clinton

**136:**

| C | O | M | P | O | S | E | R | Q | W | E | R | T | T | F |
|---|---|---|---|---|---|---|---|---|---|---|---|---|---|---|
| R | R | A | U | F | V | G | B | H | N | O | Y | U | I | R |
| Q | A | G | A | S | B | G | R | D | S | R | T | G | Y | E |
| B | G | I | S | S | I | O | O | P | V | C | E | I | T | E |
| O | O | C | V | D | E | C | W | S | E | H | E | D | F | M |
| A | S | F | E | D | R | F | J | K | L | E | I | O | P | A |
| S | D | L | G | H | J | W | N | B | Y | S | F | G | H | S |
| E | R | U | G | H | Y | O | F | G | H | T | R | G | Y | O |
| Y | H | T | O | S | I | L | O | O | P | R | Z | A | Q | N |
| O | P | E | R | A | Q | F | S | D | F | A | O | P | I | S |
| A | E | R | T | L | H | G | U | J | U | O | P | B | N |
| W | F | T | Y | I | U | A | V | I | E | N | N | A | O | I |
| F | G | H | S | E | A | N | E | C | R | V | T | N | U | I |
| A | H | R | Q | R | S | G | E | R | T | Y | U | I | O | B |
| H | J | R | T | I | D | E | R | F | T | G | Y | H | U | H |

137:

138: ($\ast$ = 6  $\ast$ = 1  $\ast$ = 21);
1 + 21 + 6 = 28

139: 1. FISH, 2. HUMANS,
3. MONKEYS, 4. SPIDERS,
5. LIZARDS, 6. BIRDS

140: A – High-frequency Active
Auroral Research Program

141:

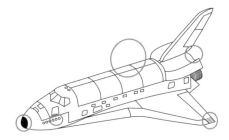

142: B

# IMAGE CREDITS

Have you enjoyed this book?

If so, find us on Facebook at Summersdale Publishers, on Twitter at @Summersdale and on Instagram and TikTok at @summersdalebooks and get in touch.

We'd love to hear from you!

www.summersdale.com